To- Harriet Berard

SARATOGA

Sojourn

Best wishes -

Allison Bennett

SARATOGA

Sojourn

ALLISON P. BENNETT

Rutledge Books, Inc.　　　　　Danbury, CT

Interior design by Elena Hartz

Cover artwork by Erin Walrath

Rutledge Books, Inc.
107 Mill Plain Road, Danbury, CT 06811
1-800-278-8533
www.rutledgebooks.com

Manufactured in the United States of America

Cataloging in Publication Data
Bennett, Allison P.
 Saratoga Sojourn

 ISBN: 1-58244-195-2

 1. Biography

Library of Congress Control Number: 2002102087

ACKNOWLEDGMENTS

No book could be written without the assistance of many personal contacts in the search for facts, local history, pictures, documents, diaries, etc. Accordingly, I wish to extend my deepest appreciation for the efforts of those who assisted me in that search.

Christine Robinson of the Historical Society of Saratoga Springs pleasantly and helpfully provided pictures and historical information. Roderic Blackburn is once again appreciated for his assistance—a friend and mentor whose name appears in my other publications. Thank you's go also to the staff of Saratoga National Historical Park, for their promptness in sending photos, as well as to Thomas J. Ambrosio, Executive Director, Montauk Lighthouse; the DAR Museum; Thomas J. DeSarbo of Prestige Photo, Delmar and Wallace Dailey of The Houghton Library at Harvard University.

A large measure of appreciation also must be given to Marilyn Smith, Managing Editor, Kim Phipps and John Laub, of Rutledge Books, Inc., without whose expertise this book would not have been born.

I would also like to express my appreciation to my husband, William D. Bennett, for his unfailing patience and support over a long period of time.

Allison P. Bennett
October 9, 2001

FOREWORD

A major problem with history is writing it. The events are stirring enough and the people are interesting enough, but you won't know it from most of what you read about it. To be fair to historians and history writers, it takes rare talent to bring "history alive." One of the ways to do that is to write in the narrative mode, giving voice to individuals long since silenced by death. The dilemma, of course, is finding sufficient facts of history to justify the characterization you create. Did she really say and feel what you state? Doing this is an artful balance, the success of which depends on the reader knowing not only what a person said and did, but how the author knew it to be true.

Allison Bennett has uncovered a rich cache of documents related to the Walworth family of Saratoga. Out of the attic trunks of long gone families she has found piles of letters, diaries, and family documents which, read randomly, are of little significance. But organized and read in detail they reveal much more than the sum of their words. Like an iceberg, the weight and dignity of the visible part owes most to that much greater part that is unseen. The author has boiled down countless sources to a spare but moving narrative of a nineteenth-century American family. Three generations of family members either experienced distinguished professional achievement or sad personal tragedy, some both. Readers are, of course, fascinated by both extremes, identifying with achievement and repulsed by failure, but intrigued by both as they serve up lessons for living.

Allison Bennett has successfully woven a web of unexpected

events, personal needs, and character fortune and failure to help us understand how a family shifted between high life among the politically and socially connected in one generation and, in another generation, religious heresy, financial failure, character and personality disorder, and even murder and incarceration. Yet through these experiences in *extremis*, we find a heroine, Ellen Hardin Walworth. Raised in the gentility of ante bellum Kentucky, married into a prominent family in New York, she experienced a failed marriage, disloyalty and disorder among some of her children, financial loss, and social disgrace, yet she perservered through the will of her personality and the soundness of her character to succeed on her own in founding a school, organizing, with a few others, the Daughters of the American Revolution, and patriotically inspiring women to help in the Spanish American War effort. The sub-text of this personal odyssey is how a woman of the Victorian age, whose role was defined by her husband's position and the children she bore, became an activist in politics, patriotic issues, and women's rights—undreamt of roles when she was young. She is a metaphor for the coming of age of the modern American woman.

Roderic H. Blackburn
Kinderhook, N.Y.
October 1, 2001

PREFACE

In a sense this book has been ten years in the making, since it was in 1991-92 that I first visited the Historical Society of Saratoga Springs and toured the third floor of their museum at the Canfield Casino. There, on exhibit, were seven rooms of furniture and memorabilia from the family of Reuben H. Walworth, a prominent Saratogian. As I learned the story of the Walworth-Hardin families that day, I became entranced and thought to myself "someone should write a book about these people." This book "Saratoga Sojourn" tells their story.

As I started the project I found that a great deal of the necessary information was right there in the museum. Of course, there was much research to do in many books and papers in many libraries. This entailed traveling to visit other locales where the family had resided at one time or another, to get a background on how these places might have affected the lives of the characters. The story was written, sat on and off the shelf, rewritten, put on the shelf again and finally sent to a publisher who accepted it.

This work is not fiction—it is a true story that underscores strong moral and religious issues of right and wrong and the consequences thereof. One of the major themes is the interplay of family dynamics, love and hatred and relationships among siblings and other family members. Weak characters are broken because of certain personality traits that predict failure. Strong characters forge ahead and make new opportunities for themselves, despite financial problems, disappointments and even death.

The Walworth family made an impression on their age and

the lives of their descendents paint a vivid picture of life in Saratoga Springs among the upper middle class of the nineteenth century. Other people of that time were leading less interesting and spectacular lives, even lives of quiet desperation in many ways, due to the inequities of living conditions. However, the human forces of good and evil that drive all mankind, rich and poor, were exemplified in the lives of the members of the Walworth family.

Allison P. Bennett

The Walworth Family

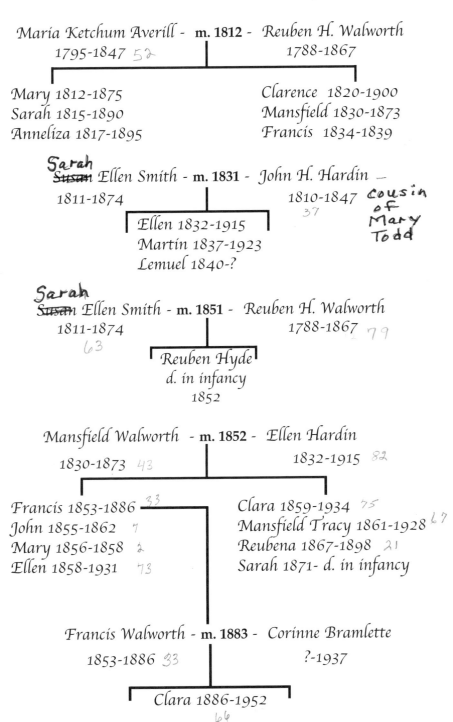

Maria Ketchum Averill - **m. 1812** - Reuben H. Walworth
1795-1847 *52*   1788-1867

Mary 1812-1875   Clarence 1820-1900
Sarah 1815-1890   Mansfield 1830-1873
Anneliza 1817-1895   Francis 1834-1839

Sarah
~~Susan~~ Ellen Smith - **m. 1831** - John H. Hardin — *cousin of Mary Todd*
1811-1874   1810-1847 *37*

Ellen 1832-1915
Martin 1837-1923
Lemuel 1840-?

Sarah
~~Susan~~ Ellen Smith - **m. 1851** - Reuben H. Walworth
1811-1874   1788-1867 *79*
63

Reuben Hyde
d. in infancy
1852

Mansfield Walworth - **m. 1852** - Ellen Hardin
1830-1873 *43*   1832-1915 *82*

Francis 1853-1886 *33*   Clara 1859-1934 *75*
John 1855-1862 *7*   Mansfield Tracy 1861-1928 *67*
Mary 1856-1858 *2*   Reubena 1867-1898 *21*
Ellen 1858-1931 *73*   Sarah 1871- d. in infancy

Francis Walworth - **m. 1883** - Corinne Bramlette
1853-1886 *33*   ?-1937

Clara 1886-1952
66

Chapter One

The words of shouted good-byes, coupled with pleas to come back and visit each year, and injunctions to write often and tell of life in Saratoga, all fell sorrowfully on Ellen Hardin's ears. She smiled wanly at her best friend, Mary Duncan, waving a lacy handkerchief in a gesture of fond farewell on the station platform. All other good-byes were checked by the high-pitched whistle of the locomotive, signaling to start the train moving slowly away from the station in Springfield, Illinois, on a May day of 1851.

As the figures on the platform faded slowly away, Ellen closed the window of the coach with a crash, sat down and slowly began to busy herself with the contents of her reticule. She pulled out a small silver vial of cologne, and unscrewing the top with a slow, deliberate motion, dabbed the scent beneath the light brown tendrils of hair that curled about her ears. She was careful not to disturb the mass of ringlets piled atop her head. The gesture was made to conceal the fact that her eyes were burning from unshed tears. She bit down hard on her lower lip in a conscious effort to control her emotions as she watched the flat plains of Illinois slip past the dingy windows.

The darkening sky of the rainy morning did not improve her mood as she thought longingly of the spacious home she had left behind, a home that her father had built on the outskirts of Jacksonville, Illinois. Ellen had been born in Jacksonville, the eldest child of Colonel John J. Hardin, who had come there from Kentucky to begin a law practice in this town that was not far from the Illinois capital of Springfield.

She pictured again in her mind their comfortable brick house, set amid shady trees and wide lawns; how her father had loved that house and the little family that it sheltered. What homesick letters he wrote to them about his longing to return to it when he was in the army in the heat and dryness of south Texas. Just when it had seemed the U.S. government forces had the Mexicans in full pursuit and that victory would not be long in coming, the dreaded telegram arrived from the War Department, telling in abrupt wording that Colonel John J. Hardin had been killed at the Battle of Buena Vista. It meant that her father would not be returning to that beloved home and family after all. The Mexican War had made a hero's widow of her mother, and Ellen and her brothers the children of a dead veteran. Ellen angrily thought to herself that if only he had not been killed, things would now be so different. Her mother would not have been free to remarry and their life would have been more predictable.

She certainly felt she had enough to cry about, for here she was, leaving the place where she had been born and brought up, for some remote city in the woods of New York State. She could not imagine she was going to like her new life one bit after the wonderful years she had spent in Jacksonville. But she knew in her heart she would have to learn to adjust to new circumstances and to Yankee ways. Her resolute nature was already beginning to accept the new challenges and she knew she would not let this move deter her pleasure in life. She vowed she would make a place for herself in this new world. She knew too that she must find new friends in a strange town, even though no one would ever take the place of her dearest friends of the past, Mary Duncan and Libby Eddy.

A monstrous lump seemed to rise in her throat as she pictured again her two dearest friends, and realized anew how much she was going to miss those girls. They had been such a lively trio, always together at school, parties, and in their free hours. In the little town of Jacksonville, where many of the residents had Southern roots, everyone knew everyone else and all fitted into the proper place within their own social circle. Then too, Mary Duncan had been the Governor's daughter, and that had lent a great deal of prestige to Ellen's own position in their tight little world. Ellen had no inkling now that she would ever be in a position to even become acquainted with the governor of New York State. All of the happy memories of her secure world in Jacksonville came crowding in on her. She shut out the pictures with a determination that was characteristic of her nature. She straightened and tossed her head as she took a firm hold of her sensibilities and tried hard to think about what direction her life would take when she settled in Saratoga.

She cast a glance at her new stepbrother, Mansfield Walworth, his tall frame reclining lazily in the opposite seat. He had his head thrown back, and his eyes were closed so he did not see her glance. Ellen wondered if he was merely feigning sleep because he had some inkling of the sorrow she was feeling at this parting from her friends and beloved hometown. Perhaps he was immersed in his own thoughts about the changes that were being brought about in his life by this new stepfamily his father was bringing home to Saratoga.

Mansfield had accompanied his father to Kentucky for Reuben Walworth's marriage to Sarah Hardin. After the wedding in Harrodsburg, Kentucky the trio had come to Illinois to pick up Ellen and her brother Lemuel, and give a brief greeting and goodbye to her brother, Martin Hardin, who was being left behind to finish his term in boarding school. The little city of Jacksonville had long been known as "the Athens of the West" for its fine educational institutions, including a college and female academy, founded by New England schoolmasters striking out for a new territory. Ellen felt her own education there had been good preparation for the days that lay ahead. Her father had loved history and encouraged her in an interest in things of an historical nature. He urged her to read the English classics of Burns and Scott, as well as the American authors, Longfellow, Holmes, Whipple, Dana, and Emerson.

As she looked at Mansfield's handsome face, Ellen recalled with a faint thrill the warmth of his greeting when he first took her hand in introduction. She had felt her face flush when he remarked to his father that he had surely got him a pretty little stepsister. But even that warming thought could not completely dispel Ellen's mood as she looked across the aisle to where her little brother, Lemuel, was sitting, his faced buried in a school-book. She felt certain he was feeling much the same as she was at that moment, even though he was seven years younger. Without a doubt, Lemuel too, was sad at the thought of leaving the only home he had even known, as well as the companions of his childhood. Seeing him fidgeting in the seat, she realized that a boy of eleven never could sit still or be thoughtful for very long. He probably was not beset with the uneasy and jealous feelings that were stirring in Ellen's breast, however.

She looked across the aisle with a sidelong glance of contempt at her mother, who was smiling archly and catching at the hand of her new husband, Reuben H. Walworth, former Chancellor of New York. Ellen could not understand how her mother could so easily erase the memory of her former husband. At least Colonel Hardin had been much younger and more dashing and handsome in his military uniform than the grey-haired old man her mother was now fawning over. It seemed ridiculous to her that her mother could feel the same warm pangs of emotion for a man that she herself, as a girl of eighteen, had felt in the past year. The thought of her mother's love for this man made Ellen's stomach churn. She felt her mother showed a monstrous disloyalty to the memory of John J. Hardin.

The sight of her mother's romantic actions, however, had made Ellen's mind revert to her own feelings of first love. Lately, when she had been visiting in Kentucky, her cousin Tracey had given her a great deal of attention and seemed to take a fancy to being in her company. She was not at all interested in him as Tracey was only seventeen and she felt him inclined to be dissipated, and never exercising a great deal of patience. Still, she had been secretly pleased that someone of the opposite sex had found her attractive. She had also become very aware of the young men in Jacksonville and harbored secret crushes on some of them.

In the fall and winter of 1849, Ellen was away from Illinois, visiting with relatives in Kentucky. By December she was writing from Kentucky to her friend, Mary Duncan, "Love for Charlie Hine crept into my heart so slyly and imperceptibly. I prayed often and earnestly that I might be directed in the right way. Charlie is so noble that I see a very bright and beautiful future. I know you will think me fickle, but there is no room in my heart now for the boy from home."

In January of 1850, she confided to Mary Duncan her "rapturous feelings of love for Charlie Hine." A month later she wrote "Charlie is to be confirmed in New Albany (Indiana) tonight. I will spend the hours alone with our God and with him. It will make my heart thrill to think how closely our hearts will be knit together this night. I have had a positive offer from a beau in Frankfort, but you know I love another. Mother is always trying to fix me up."

In May, Ellen's mother had met Charlie Hine. She was not impressed and felt that Ellen was acting overly sentimental and attaching undue importance to what her mother thought was only a little flirtation. There was no question that Sarah Hardin felt Charlie Hine was not to be considered eligible for her daughter's hand. She exacted a promise from Ellen to cease all correspondence with him for at least a year. By then, she felt Ellen would have time to get things in perspective, find new interests, and realize for herself how unsuitable Charlie was for her.

Thinking of those events now, Ellen's mind reverted to the year 1850, when she had visited the plantation of her mother's brother, Abram Smith, in Mississippi. The little visitor from Illinois had been feted with parties and visits. The pleasant memories of a gay and gracious way of life in an unhurried atmosphere of rural plenty reminded her of many happy times. It had been there that she had met Will Blanton, a young physician, and she had stayed on to visit for some months. Her relationship with him developed seriously and before too many months had passed, she was accepting his proposal of a formal engagement, as easily as she had accepted Charlie Hine's the previous December. She felt she was almost in love with Will, yet somewhere in the back of her mind was the thought that she really was not yet ready to make a serious commitment to marriage.

Perhaps it was fortunate she had to return to Jacksonville to school, as it gave her time to think the matter over. The engagement was broken by the beginning of 1851, as plans were already afoot for her mother's marriage and the move to Saratoga. It provided Ellen with an easy way to cease the relationship with Will Blanton. However, she would always remember Mississippi and her days spent there with a great deal of happiness. Her uncle's family knew how to make life pleasant with their courtly social graces and punctilious manners. The patriarchal plantation society had revolved in an ordered world of its own, far removed from the unpleasantness that lapped at their very feet.

With these pictures in her mind, Ellen could not help but wonder what her new home would be like. Certainly a man of the Chancellor's position would be well-to-do and have a luxurious home. Perhaps this old man was not quite as bad as she had painted him in her ungenerous thoughts. She had to admit he did have a dignity in his appearance and he exhibited a gentle and refined manner. So far, he had been pleasant to her and the boys but she did think from his looks he might be stern if he really became annoyed. She was still certain she would not like this new life in Saratoga at all because she had heard from other Southerners who had journeyed north about how cold and conceited the Yankees could act. She also felt that some Saratogians might not be overjoyed to make their acquaintance either, since her mother was now the new wife of the past Chancellor of New York, who was one of Saratoga's leading citizens. She guessed that probably many would be jealous that Sarah Hardin had caught him in the marriage net when they might have had their own caps set for him.

With these thoughts running through her head, Ellen leaned

back against the grimy seat and shut her eyes. Tears were very near the surface again and she wanted to hide the apprehension she felt about the unknown life that was ahead of her in upstate New York.

Chapter Two

᪻

Reuben Hyde Walworth, sitting across the aisle from his new stepdaughter, Ellen Hardin, looked pensively out of the train window at the soggy landscape, musing as the train steamed along the rails on the long journey to Saratoga. In the back of his mind he wondered if people would think him an old fool, taking on a new wife and family at the age of sixty-three. However, from their lengthy correspondence, he felt Sarah Hardin was a woman with common sense, who was fond of books and learning, and a religious person at heart. He was glad she had agreed to leave the Episcopal Church and rejoin the Presbyterian faith for he would not want them to take commun-ion at different tables. Since John Hardin, her first husband, had been a lawyer and a Congressman, she had been exposed to life in the Capital and was used to being a part of a larger sphere of society. Then too, her husband had been a cousin to Mary Todd Lincoln. In fact, Lincoln met Mary Todd at John Hardin's house in Illinois. Lincoln too, had served a term in Congress and was now gaining fame as a lawyer in Springfield. Looking back, he felt it was a lucky moment when he went to Louisville on that busi-ness trip and was introduced to Sarah Hardin, who impressed him immediately. But for all that, he knew there would never, ever, be any woman who could appeal to him in the way his beloved Maria had done.

His thoughts turned abruptly to his first love and he went back over his life, picturing the early years of his boyhood at the little farming settlement of Hoosick, New York, nestled in the rolling hills not far from the Vermont border. The little country village held only the usual white-painted clapboard church, a brick store, small cobbler's shop, wooden schoolhouse, and a few dwelling houses strung out along the main street. But even then it had shown promise of becoming a trading center for the farmers of the locality. Its heart was cut by a rushing falls that provided the setting for a gristmill. Other manufacturing operations would in time follow and increase the prosperity of the place. The farm home of Reuben's youth was built in 1795, on the perimeter of the village, and it had been ample for such a large family. The ten young Walworths enjoyed playing in the big yard surrounded by a picket fence and shaded with maple and locust trees that towered over the substantial house. Behind the house, the fields reached to the Hoosick River, and the steep banks that contained the stream made wonderful places for a young boy to clamber and explore after the chores and lessons were finished.

Reuben had always admired his father, Benjamin's, staunchness in the face of daily living. Benjamin's driving desire was to make the farm produce so his family would be well provided for and the children would have the education they needed to go on to a life of more fulfillment in the world outside the little country town. Great opportunities in business and politics were opening up in the new republic. Benjamin Walworth knew that bright, industrious children could find a place in the new society that would be less arduous than the life he had pursued. Certainly it would not, however, be any less effortless in other ways if they were to find their niche in a world of prestige and prosperity.

Reuben thought back to the long winter evenings in the big farm kitchen when the children, sitting around the large dining table, had asked their father to recite to them his experiences in the War of Revolution, when he fought with General Washington's army at the Battle of White Plains and around New York City. They loved to hear him tell of his experiences of July 1779 when Brant and his Indian friends made a raid on Minisink to the north and Benjamin was one of a party of volunteers who went in pursuit of the savages. The group fell into an ambush and many were killed, but Benjamin, who was serving as quartermaster, was saved from death because he had ridden back to secure more ammunition for the harassed troops.

Reuben remembered too, how proud his father had been of the fact that their ancestors had come over from England in 1669 to settle around Fishers Island and Groton, Connecticut. The first Walworth, William, had immigrated to this country at the insistence of Fitzjohn Winthrop, grandson of Massachusett's first governor, to introduce English cultivation on the island off the coast of Connecticut. That pioneer spirit had been nurtured and renewed in each succeeding generation. Benjamin's older brother, John, had gone to upper New York State before the Revolutionary War, when the sparsely settled territory was still threatened by attack from hostile Indians. John had been imbued with the desire to strike out independently with his Yankee wife and leave the old seashore town in Connecticut for a new and fertile promised land at Hoosick. Benjamin Walworth, too had found no future at Groton. Early he made his way westward to work as a hatter in Poughkeepsie and later at Minisink in Orange County. During the Revolution, he served as quartermaster of his regiment, but after his discharge he came back to Minisink. By then the trading spirit consumed him, and he crossed the Hudson River to open a store at the settlement of Nine Partners in Dutchess County, in company with Philip Hart. Later, the two men moved up river and established another store at Schaghticoke in Rensselear County, not too far from Benjamin's brother, John, at Hoosick. In 1782, Benjamin returned to Connecticut to claim a bride he had waited for much too long a time. The young girls in the Walworth family especially found the story of this spurned love to be most romantic and never tired hearing their father tell it.

He repeated to them how their mother, Apphia Hyde, was left an orphan at a tender age and her uncle, Tracy Hyde, took her to live with him. Her father had been a minister, the Reverend Jebidiah Hyde, a great-grandson of one of the founders of Norwich, Connecticut. In time, Apphia grew up to be a good seamstress and when Benjamin needed a new coat, she made one for him and that was how he met her. They began to keep company but Benjamin's mother did not take kindly to Apphia, feeling she was nowhere near Benjamin's station in life and that he should look elsewhere for a wife.

Apphia would have none of that, for she too was proud and so she broke off with Benjamin. In a few months, she wed Captain Nicholas Cardell of New London, but he was lost at sea in 1781 and Apphia was a widow and mother of a son at twenty-three years of age. Even though Benjamin should have been sad to hear this news, his heart leaped for joy when he heard she was unattached, and he made a quick visit of condolence to her. After that, he made several more trips to Connecticut, and the next year they were married. He sold his share of the interest in the store and moved to Bozrah to work his wife's farm.

The memories of upstate New York with its broad acres kept recurring in Benjamin's mind as he farmed the stony uplands of Connecticut and in 1793, he packed up his wife and children, taking them by farm wagon over the rutted roads on a tedious journey to the pleasant little village beside the Hoosick River where his brother, John, had settled. Benjamin took up a parcel of land on the Schneyder Patent in the eastern section of the town of Hoosick. By 1795, he found a chance to better his position by buying a farm of two hundred acres from John Waldo. This new land included all that part of the village of Hoosick Falls lying east of the Hoosick River.

Shortly after his arrival in Hoosick Falls, and seeing another chance for personal gain, Benjamin entered into partnership with Theophilus Comstock to purchase the Colvin gristmill on the south side of the little river. Benjamin was a conscientious man and over the years he proved to be a valuable addition to the growing settlement. He used his means, influence, and personal labor for the improvement of the village and the good of its inhabitants. The summer days blended into the sharp coldness of upstate winters as the years rolled by, and the Walworths raised their children and farmed their acres. Eventually, there was to be a break that would change the homely lifestyle of one of their children, Reuben Hyde Walworth, forever.

Chapter Three

R euben's teacher at the village school had quickly recognized he was a better than average student and that book learning seemed to come naturally to him. Reuben too, at seventeen, was beginning to realize that farming was not his passion, and so other plans began to form for both the parents and child. Benjamin Walworth's farm was prosperous and since he also had a partnership in the gristmill along the Hoosick River, there was some financial ability to give this son a chance at a career that might prove more profitable than farming in the long haul, and that would be much more to his liking and abilities.

John Russell was a prominent lawyer, practicing in an office on Second Street in the expanding village of Troy, New York. It was the policy of the time to take promising young men into his office and start them learning the fundamentals of a career in law. Arrangements were made for Reuben Walworth to begin reading the law with Mr. Russell and in the fall, Reuben and his father rode westward in the pleasure wagon toward the spot still known as Vanderheyden's Ferry by many old settlers, but lately called Troy by the many New Englanders who came to settle there.

The village, extending about one mile along the winding

course of River Street, already boasted a new courthouse and jail that appeared truly imposing to an unsophisticated country boy. It was built of brick, two stories high, and its tall tower incorporated a large bell and was surmounted with an iron weather vane. Its yard along Second Street also contained a whipping post, a pair of stocks for miscreants, and a gallows for hangings. The church steeples pointed their long, slender fingers toward the heavens, a carryover in architecture from the New England meetinghouses that were familiar to the settlers from that region who had come here seeking a better livelihood soon after the Revolutionary War.

The place seemed a virtual metropolis to young Reuben as he and his father rode down the noisy, bustling streets, awash with horses and drays, carriages and stage coaches, and farm wagons taking produce to the boats tied up at the docks along the Hudson River. Like any newcomer, Reuben tried to hide his anxiety in an appearance of deep interest in the passing scene, hoping in his heart he would be happy in making a new and different life from that which he had known in the country village of his early years.

The four years that Reuben spent reading law in Troy flew by very quickly. It had given him a taste of a more complex life and a sense of worldly wisdom that had been unknown to him on the farm in Hoosick. He met other aspiring young men, among them William L. Marcy, who came into the law office after his graduation from Brown University. They would meet again many times, not only in military service, but also when Marcy went on to become Judge of the Supreme Court of New York, a United States Senator, Governor of New York, and during Marcy's service in the cabinets of Presidents Polk and Pierce. Connections with people of importance like Marcy would prove to be helpful to

Reuben's own career, even though at that early date he was unaware of the implications.

An icy January wind in the winter of 1811 penetrated through Reuben's long, black woolen greatcoat with its attached cape collar. He stood bent against it, his foot on a small cowhide trunk and holding a valise in his hand. Hoof beats reverberated in the cold, clear air as the horses pulling the stage from Albany rounded the turn, and the vehicle rolled to a stop at the door of Platt Titus' inn in Troy. As the door opened, passengers stiff with cold descended the iron steps and hastened to the inn door, seeking the sheltering warmth within. The few waiting passengers were boarded, and with a lurch that pitched them all forward in their seats, the vehicle rattled and jolted away toward its destination up the Hudson River valley to Lansingburgh, Sandy Hill (now Glens Falls), and a stop at Whitehall. From there, the journey would _Hudson_ continue northerly on the Whitehall-Lake George Turnpike road to the final destination at Plattsburgh, a journey of three days. Reuben had climbed aboard eagerly, as if he couldn't wait to get started at the business of beginning a new law practice in the raw, northerly settlement at Plattsburgh, close upon the Canadian border. In 1784, Judge Zephaniah Platt had come from Poughkeepsie to take up a patent of thirty thousand acres at this place. He was associated in this endeavor with other capitalists having "war bounty" grants.

The year of 1811 was a dubious time to be heading in that direction, for there was much war talk circulating against Britain and its treatment of American ships and sailors upon the high seas and its embargoes against American goods. However, this was a time when America was confident of her rightful place in the world and had the strong support of her citizens. Plattsburgh was not a very large town, but its location on Lake Champlain and its nearness to the Canadian border seemed advantageous. It was already beginning to be called the capital of the North Country, because it was on the direct route between Albany and Montreal. A prominent judge, Charles Platt, for whose family the little town was named, was a jurist of importance, and Reuben looked forward to working with him. The new frontier aspect of the place intrigued young Reuben and the views of Lake Champlain, lying in a wide, fertile valley, surrounded by the Green Mountains of Vermont and the Adirondacks of New York, presented a spectacular sight in the cold frostiness of the winter days.

When the stage pulled into the little settlement of Plattsburgh, Reuben disembarked, stretching tall and looking about. He saw a huddle of small wooden houses clustered near the lakeshore and across the deep ravine cut by the Saranac River as it raced down from the mountains to meet its end in the icy waters of the lake. There were a smattering of stores and inns clustered about the main street; dwelling houses led off into the surrounding fields away from the lakeshore. A newly construct-ed "Academy" stood starkly in the frozen mud of winter. The only public building Reuben saw was the courthouse, and he knew instinctively he would be spending many long hours there in the days and years to come.

Lounging about the stage depot were several young men, seemingly with nothing more to do than stand with their hands in their pockets and observe the newcomers who came spilling out of the coach. The arrival of the stage from the south was one of the high points of excitement in the little town, for the travel-ers brought with them an air of mystery that spoke of a world outside the confines of this valley, a world that was different and more enticing than the unhurried pace they knew.

In seeking to find information about the law office of his partner-to-be, John Palmer, a childhood friend in Hoosick and also a lawyer beginning his practice in this new place, Reuben approached a young man who introduced himself as Henry Taylor. Little did Reuben realize then that Henry Taylor would later be working for him in the capacity of handyman and driver for many years. This moment too was the beginning for Reuben of a career that would span a long period of years and bring him high achievements and many honors in his chosen profession.

Chapter Four

❦

Reuben had been raised in a household that believed in the admonition that one way to show respect to the Lord was to attend Sunday worship service. This lesson had not been lost on him and he sought out the local Presbyterian congregation. It did not as yet have its own sanctuary, but was in the process of making plans to build a new church. On a certain Sunday, he took his seat among the worshippers and, after settling into a seat and bowing his head in silent prayer as a sign of his willingness to receive the Word, he raised his head and looked out over the small congregation.

As in any such group, there were several middle-aged couples, a few spinsters, family groups with small children and older ladies with white hair who sat together in a group, gossiping and whispering loudly. Looking off to the left he noticed, seated between her parents, a young girl with her hair swept up to the top of a most charmingly shaped head. His interest was piqued in a way he had never known before with any young woman. She turned at that moment to speak to her mother and the sweet, innocent look on her face put a glow into Reuben's heart that spread throughout his body and warmed his extremities. Never had he seen any girl who moved him so. He knew he must meet this family after the service and find out who this enchanting creature might be. He decided the best way to do it was to take a bold approach and get to her side quickly and introduce himself to her parents. The service of worship and the message of the sermon were lost to him that day, in his impatience for the hour of worship to end.

The girl, Maria Ketchum Averill, was a dark-haired budding beauty of fifteen. Her proudly set head carried an oval face that was framed with wispy curls. She reminded Reuben of nothing so much as a fresh rosebud, about to burst into bloom. Yet she had a certain demureness and seemed completely unaware of her physical attractions. When the service was over, Reuben maneuvered himself to a position where the family would pass. As soon as they came up, he introduced himself to the father in a cordial manner and when the introduction came to Maria, he bowed low over her hand. Maria's mother, Polly Averill, with matronly curiosity, immediately asked what had brought Reuben to their little town of Plattsburgh. His glances at Maria had not been completely lost to the mother's eye. Reuben was quick to explain he was there to practice law with his partner, John Palmer. Mr. Averill made some welcoming remarks to Reuben and with that, shepherded his wife and daughter through the door.

Reuben knew he would come back to services again and in the meantime would try to find out as much as possible about Maria Averill. Not long after he fulfilled his wish to at least know her family better. Judge Platt invited Reuben to attend a dinner party at his home to meet some of the more prominent citizens of the community. Reuben hoped to see the Averill family there, but his anticipation was turned to ashes as he found only the elders

present. However, he wisely hid his disappointment. His intelligent observations and keen questions throughout the evening
caught the gentlemen's attention; he made important connections there with some of the town leaders that would serve him
well in the months and years ahead.

Maria Averill was, like Reuben, a descendent of early Anglo-
Saxon settlers from New England. Her grandfather, Joseph
Ketchum, had been among the first settlers in Plattsburgh and
operated a forge there in 1798. His wife had served as post-
mistress. Their daughter, Polly, married Nathan Averill and they
resided in the village at Oak and Court Streets. A British solider
was buried in the garden of the Averill house during the War of
1812. The nephew of Maria's grandmother had been president of
Yale College, a point of much pride in the family. Maria's upbringing had been staunchly Presbyterian, and she was to be sincerely
devoted to her religious teachings throughout her lifetime.

She was an extremely conscientious girl with a gentle and
affectionate nature and the pliability necessary to become the
wife of an intellectual and ambitious young man with strong
opinions. Reuben lost no time in his pursuit for her hand.
However, in deference to her relatives and because of her youth,
he had to wait patiently for her to finish a prescribed course of
study. Even so, within a year the courtship ended in marriage.
Before five years had passed, three daughters were born to the
couple, and three years later, in 1820, Maria presented Reuben
with his first son, Clarence A. Walworth.

As Reuben reminisced, he could not help but suppress an
inward chuckle at the thought of the country house he had
planned for his young bride. It was just outside the village of
Plattsburgh where he had taken her to live immediately after
their marriage. Coming home through the woods one day after a

lengthy round of duties, he rode into the clearing and found his house burned to the ground, with ashes still smoldering, and with his wife and new baby nowhere in sight. Cold fear gripped his heart, and his knees nearly failed him as he alighted from his horse and ran toward the blackened ruin. He prayed hastily to God that his wife had not been consumed in the inferno. Choking sobs escaped from his constricted throat as he thought of every possibility, not wanting to believe that God could vent such punishment on him that He would take the wife and child in such a dreadful holocaust. As he stood thus, reason overcame his fright and he knew he must go and try to find out what had happened, even though the news might be the worst he could hear. Galloping away on his horse he made a desperate search throughout the neighborhood. Finally, he found Maria and baby safe at the home of a neighbor about a mile away.

After that episode, Reuben decided they must move into the village to another house located near the Fouquet House, an inn in the heart of town. In the years they spent there, Reuben's domestic life became the retreat he needed from the exhausting application to his law practice and his political aspirations. While he was in Plattsburgh, these included the posts of Justice of the Peace, Master in Chancery, Supreme Court Commissioner and member of Congress, representing the Twelfth Congressional District consisting of five northern counties, from 1821 to 1823.

Chapter Five

Reuben was beginning to take a commanding place of leadership in the community, but he had no sooner settled into his new career and marriage than war broke out over the waters of Lake Champlain and the lands of northern New York. In 1812, the village of Plattsburgh was headquarters for the American generals commanding the northern frontier and a rendezvous for troops defending the border against the British armies. In November of 1812, a campaign was mounted from here by the Americans against Montreal. It proved to be a failure; the American militia refused to cross the U.S. border and march into Canada. The army retreated to Plattsburgh to spend the winter in hastily constructed barracks.

In 1811, Reuben had subscribed five shares toward the completion of the Academy building. At its erection, it was considered "the largest and most imposing public edifice in northern New York." However, its beginning activity was abruptly brought to a close by the War of 1812. It was leased to the U.S. government for an infantry barracks, as was the partially completed Presbyterian Church building adjoining it that had been started in 1812.

In July of 1813, the little town was narrowly saved from destruction when a British naval squadron of fourteen hundred men gained control of Lake Champlain, burned the barracks, and plundered the government magazines. American troops at that time were in Burlington, Vermont. In the Plattsburgh Republican of August 21, 1813, there was printed a testimony to the effect that Reuben Walworth "saw British soldiers plundering the house of one Peter Sailly and saw them bring out books, large quantities of clothing, and other property. Several officers were present and looking on, and one came up and drank milk brought up from the cellar of the house. None of the officers attempted to prevent the soldiers from carrying off the plunder. Some soldiers also beat in the windows of Mr. Palmer's house with a club. Even though there were several officers in plain sight, none attempted to interfere. When they set fire to Mr. Sailly's store, the deponent, with several others, went with water to keep the fire off the dwelling house, but a sentinel was placed there with orders to let no citizens near the house. A great number of soldiers were in the house, plundering it." In November of 1813, another attack on Montreal was repulsed before the Americans reached the city and the army again retreated to Plattsburgh to spend the winter.

By 1814, a real crisis in the war had developed. With the final defeat of Napoleon's forces at Waterloo, the British could now turn their entire attention to the United States. Seasoned veterans of Wellington's army were sent to fight in North America. However, the tide was about to turn. Heretofore, the United States had been attempting to invade and conquer Canada, but now the British made plans to invade New York with a large army of veterans from Europe. Under these conditions, the country now became united for the first time and Federalist battalions turned out as well as Republicans, and the conflict was engaged with renewed vigor as a well-trained American force was placed on the northern frontier. The danger to the Lake Champlain area was real enough, though, because the British had amassed a large body of troops poised on the northern borders of the United States. The greatest threat to Reuben's life came in September of 1814, during the British invasion of Plattsburgh.

With only two hundred and fifty infantrymen at that place under the command of General Macomb, General Izard's troops having gone to the Mohawk Valley and west, the British general provost advanced from Canada on September 4, 1814 with fourteen thousand men, and encamped eight miles from the village. Several of his gunboats moved up the lake to Isle La Motte off the Vermont shore. The Americans threw up earthworks and a call for reinforcements was hastily sent out, with two thousand four hundred men available for active duty. Among the young men whom Reuben knew who served with him at that time was William L. Marcy, who had been in Troy with Reuben when he was a reading clerk in John Russell's law office. Another was Major John Ellis Wool from Troy, who had made the army his career. Wool was to be brevetted a colonel of infantry for bravery at the Battle of Plattsburgh on September 11, 1814.

The British moved on Plattsburgh on September 5. Major Wool engaged the enemy and fell back in a delaying tactic to the south bank of the Saranac River. There were forty-five Americans and two hundred fifty British soldiers killed that day. In five days of siege, the British were prevented from crossing the Saranac. The patriots strengthened their fortifications and reinforcements for the Americans poured in. Commodore Macdonough, meanwhile, was fighting the British fleet on the lake in a two-and-one-half-hour battle. His foresight had him anchor his ships across the mouth of Plattsburgh Bay so the British had to approach his fleet head-on. While the British troops made three assaults at different points, none were successful. At this point, Reuben Walworth, serving as adjutant general in General Mooers' division, rode up to announce that the British fleet had surrendered. The thirteen thousand remaining British soldiers retreated from Plattsburgh that night of September 11, defeated by four thousand Americans and the collapse of their own fleet. This action ended all hostile operations on the Champlain frontier. Reuben Walworth returned to his family and law career. When Plattsburgh became an incorporated village in 1815, Reuben was elected to serve as one of the first six village trustees.

On July 26, 1817, President James Monroe came up the lake from Whitehall aboard the steamboat Phoenix, to visit the village. An excited crowd was waiting at Cumberland Head, the steamboat landing, to welcome the illustrious visitor. The President was escorted to Isaac Green's inn, where he stayed for two days. The hostelry was the social center of the village, and its curved-ceilinged room in the attic served as the Masonic Lodge. Reuben Walworth, on behalf of the village, was chosen to deliver the welcoming address, which he did from the square porch on the street side. Afterward, the President reviewed the troops stationed at the barracks and attended a large public party. On Sunday morning, he attended the Presbyterian Church service and took tea that afternoon at Judge deLord's house, leaving on Monday morning for Sackett's Harbor.

The President left town with a military escort. After proceeding eleven miles into the woods along the Chateaugay Road, the party was halted. There, a sumptuous breakfast awaited him, laid beside a gently murmuring brook in the still, encompassing forest. The surprise and setting were conducive to generous thoughts; after being led through a triumphal arch of green boughs to a shaded seat, the President toasted the citizens of Plattsburgh in the most flattering terms. When the repast was over, he continued on his way and the President's visit of 1817 passed into history.

By November 5, 1817 a northern canal connecting Lake Champlain and the Hudson River was commenced and completed two years later. This would be a major improvement for transportation in the Champlain Valley, enabling produce to be shipped to metropolitan areas downstate. Reuben was instrumental in working at this project and he also served as a trustee of the Academy in Plattsburgh in 1821. Here, his eldest daughter, Mary E. Walworth, took second prize in geography in 1822. In 1821, Reuben's achievements in the growing area of northern New York resulted in his being elected to serve a two-year term as a Democratic-Republican Congressman under the presidency of James Monroe. His term was uneventful and the laborious trips between Plattsburgh and Washington took him often away from his beloved wife and children.

While Reuben had enjoyed the people he met in Washington, he felt the impositions of being away from his home and law practice for such extended periods of time were damaging to his business. He felt, too, that the political scene was not what best suited his nature, so he declined renomination the following year. Not only had he gained civic prominence, but during his thirteen years in Plattsburgh, he had also come to legal prominence. His diligence and intelligence were rewarded handsomely in 1823 when he was appointed Circuit Judge of the Fourth

Judicial District of the State of New York. He held his first circuit in Clinton County in June 1823. That October, he moved his family to Saratoga Springs to be more centrally located within the district for the performance of his duties.

Chapter Six

⟨⟨⟩⟩

When the decision had been made to move the family from Plattsburgh, Reuben had gone to Saratoga Springs and found a house with which he became enamored at first sight. It was the home of Judge Walton, situated on North Broadway, the main street of the little city. The Greek Revival style house was two stories in height, with a wing at either side. The house was built of wood, with walls lined with brick, an early attempt at insulation. Judge Walton had purchased the land for the house from Rip Van Dam, an early Dutch settler in the area. Rip had purchased his title from the Indians and the huge old pine trees on the property were survivors from the original forest.

This house, Pine Grove, became the much-loved home of the Walworth family and served them as shelter against the life storms that battered at the family members over the one hundred twenty-five years of their occupancy. The first five years at Pine Grove saw the birth of another child, who did not survive, and the maturation of Maria into a busy mother, hostess, and volunteer in several charitable agencies in the Saratoga community by the time she was thirty years of age.

The Walworth family was faithful in their attendance at

Sunday services at the Presbyterian Church. Maria especially loved to attend the Wednesday night services in the Church Street meetinghouse, and her son, Clarence A. Walworth, carried a foot-warmer for his mother's use in the coldest months. Little Clarence was happy to be near her and snuggled close to keep warm in the drafty building. He enjoyed hearing her sweet voice singing the old, familiar hymns. When the deacons came in procession down the center aisle, it was as if, on cue, he knew he must sit up straighter and behave well. If only Maria could have realized this exposure to religion would have a much deeper impression on the young boy than she could ever imagine. A large part of her religious commitment would eventually reappear in Clarence's future life choices.

Maria had one material passion, a love of fine and expensive furniture. She would come home from a shopping expedition and tell Reuben she had seen just what was needed in a shop on Broadway and exclaim how lovely it would look in the parlor. Reuben always replied she should go ahead and purchase it if it was needed for the house and that he trusted her judgment and had not time himself to think about such matters. When the time came to make the purchase, however, her Puritan conscience would enter the picture; she usually bought something less expensive and spent the remainder of the money on gifts of food and clothing for some needy family. At heart, she was a loving reformer, tender to children and the underprivileged. She had long ago set her face against all that would interfere with the salvation of souls, and she denied herself all gay and thoughtless amusements.

Within six years of moving into Pine Grove, Reuben came to Maria one day with an exciting piece of news. He told Maria he had long coveted an appointment to the Chancery Court, but that with New York politics in an uproar, he felt he had little chance of securing it even though Governor Pitcher was an old colleague from Reuben's days in the U.S. Congress. Reuben did have two influential political friends in Millard Fillmore and William Seward, and he felt they might have had a hand in influencing members of the legislature. Waving an envelope before Maria, he proudly announced to her that she was looking at the newly appointed Chancellor of the State of New York.

Reuben explained to her that the Chancery Court was much different from the Courts of Common Law where he had been presiding. He would be free of technical restraints and would be dealing with cases involving debts, intricate accounts, legacies and the administration of estates. There would also be cases involving frauds, contracts, and divorces, as well as those involving the rights of children, widows, and the handicapped. His court must also review all appeals from the State Supreme Court. In essence, he, Reuben Walworth would be the sole arbitrator of the fate of properties and persons—an awesome responsibility to a man of conscience.

Maria was quite unprepared for the decision that was to come next after this portentous announcement. Reuben felt they must take a house in Albany so he could be near the other courts and the seat of government. He also knew he would see little of his family if they stayed at Saratoga Springs. However, he assured Maria they would never give up Pine Grove and that she and the children would spend summer vacations there as well as all holidays. Also, he noted that the new salary of three thousand dollars a year would make the adjustment more pleasant.

The move to Albany was accomplished, with the family occupying a house on Washington Avenue, above the Capitol Building. The location proved convenient for walking to the courtrooms and academies. Mary, Sarah, and Eliza attended the Female Academy on Pearl Street, an imposing structure fronted with heavy Greek columns. Clarence attended the Boys Academy, a red sandstone structure just across the street from the Capitol building. He learned to hold in respect the noted principal, Dr. T. Romeyn Beck, who had such great influence on many of the young lives entrusted to his care.

One day, Clarence came home from school with a red welt across his ear and scalp. Alarmed, Maria asked what had caused this and said that she hoped he had not been fighting with other boys, although because of Clarence's kind and gentle manner, she could hardly believe this to be the case. Clarence confessed he had been whispering in class and the teacher came down on him with a ruler for not paying attention. Maria was full of admonishment for his lack of attention, but in her own heart could not help feeling that the punishment had been a bit severe. When Reuben came home that evening, his attention was called to the episode. After carefully examining Clarence's scalp and listening to the reasons for the mark, he retorted brusquely, "See here, young man, if you ever come home from school again in that condition, I too, will give you a punishment you will not soon forget."

This was only one of the instances that were instrumental in forming the character of young Clarence. In 1830, he was sent to Williamstown, Massachusetts, to begin his college preparation in a beautiful old mansion full of charm and graciousness, Sloan House, the home of one Professor Sloan and his family. While at the preparatory school, he received two letters from his father that Clarence kept for the rest of his life. They were full of good sound advice upon which to build a life and Clarence took the words to his heart. The scholarly atmosphere of Williamstown formed his tastes, and the love of learning that had begun early never left him. He entered Union College, of which his father was a trustee, at age fourteen and graduated at eighteen in 1838. After graduation, Clarence began to read law in various law offices, first in Albany and then in Canandaigua, New York.

Chapter Seven

⌒⌒

The move of the Walworth family to Albany lasted five years and in 1830, Mansfield Tracy Walworth was born in that city, the fifth of Maria's children. In 1833, Reuben felt he could adequately discharge his duties from his home in Saratoga Springs, and so the family went back to Pine Grove for good. Another child, Frances deLord, was born there the next year, but lived only to the age of five. Reuben recalled the letter he had received in Albany from his good friend, C.M. Beach, of Saratoga, announcing to him the birth of a ten-pound daughter. He assured Reuben that all was well and Maria had been tended during the delivery by the same nurse once employed by Mrs. Beach. Court duties had prevented Reuben's presence at the event. This child was to be the last of Maria's babies.

The house in Saratoga Springs was filled with both laughter and tears as the Walworth children grew into maturity. Also, Reuben himself was one of the attractions at the summer resort. As New York's most powerful judicial figure, his opinions and decisions were widely circulated by the press, and visitors to Saratoga were drawn to glimpse the excitement of his court proceedings. The Chancellor filled his home with visits from friends and he often went around to the hotels in town during the season, checking the registers and calling on everyone he knew; they were invited to visit his home in return. There came through the door of Pine Grove such luminaries as William Marcy, DeWitt Clinton, and Joseph Bonaparte. It was said in later years that five U.S. Presidents had visited there.

A pang of bitterness still welled up in Reuben's heart when he thought of his beloved Maria's death. They had been so pleased when their first born son, Clarence, announced his intention of studying law. Eventually Clarence went to practice in Rochester, New York, and Reuben knew the satisfaction of seeing a son follow in his footsteps.

However, one afternoon Maria had appeared in Reuben's office in a state of great agitation. She held up a letter from Clarence in which he stated he was giving up his law practice and entering the Episcopal Seminary in New York City. He said he had been considering this decision for some time and had not wished to upset them, but that he was going into the seminary within two weeks and would appreciate his parent's understanding of his actions and assisting him in paying the tuition.

Reuben was as shocked as Maria, for he had never known Clarence felt any strong leaning toward a church vocation. However, he realized that Clarence had always been a model of studious behavior and never did a rash thing in his life, so he must have given this decision considerable thought.

This proved to be only the first inkling of a strange transformation for their beloved Clarence. From the letter, they learned he had started attending an Episcopal church in Canandaigua with a fellow lodger, and he had even joined their choir. He said he had been much attracted to the ritualistic ceremonies of that denomination, as opposed to the stark simplicity of the Calvinist churches. He also had been much enthused by the evangelist, Charles G. Finney, who had been conducting revivals in Rochester from 1841 to 1842. Several young lawyers of his acquaintance had been converted by Finney's rhetoric. His Episcopal pastor in Rochester, Dr. Whitehouse, had encouraged him and had written a letter, recommending Clarence for orders in his diocese.

Clarence came home for a brief visit before entering the seminary in New York. He tried to explain his position to his parents. In the end, his mother was won over because of her own love for the Church and what it stood for. Chancellor Walworth yielded to Clarence's request and paid his way through the seminary, manfully hiding his own mixed feelings about the course Clarence was taking.

In the summer of 1842, Reuben invited Clarence to be his guest at the annual convention of the American Board of Foreign Missions. Clarence attended all the sessions and listened earnestly to a recommendation for the employment of unmarried men in foreign mission labor, which raised a storm of opposition among the delegates. The lecturer served to raise a great question on Clarence's mind. He reasoned that if celibacy was necessary for the most successful mission work, why was it not important for all labors in the Christian ministry?

Just at this time, too, there was a movement within the Church of England toward ritualism and spiritualism that was being actively initiated and led by the dons of Oxford University. Known as "The Oxford Movement," it opposed the dry rationalism of the established church and the growing tendency toward control of the church by the state. In many widely distributed tracts, some of which had fallen into the hands of Clarence and his fellow students, the group promoted a reform of Anglicanism and suggested a return to the rituals of the Roman Catholic Church, such as private confession, fasting, veneration of the saints, and kneeling at worship. An American counterpart to the Oxford Movement developed in the Episcopal Church.

All that he had heard at the mission conference and during three years of study at the seminary caused Clarence to be constantly beset with doubts. He was often influenced by lengthy theological debates with his fellow seminarians. Several of the young men finally made their choice to follow Romanism, and Clarence was among them. He knew his parents would be violently opposed to his decision, but his conscience would not let him consider any other course. Accordingly, he took the train to Saratoga Springs to tell them that he had been unalterably attracted to Roman Catholicism and must convert and pursue studies leading to the priesthood. He tried to talk with his mother and remove some of her prejudices against the Catholic faith, but he could make no perceptible headway.

Maria could or would not believe what Clarence was telling her. For centuries her family had been separatists, emigrating to New England to secure their own freedom of religion. How could this so go against all his ancestors had held dear? She could never again be able to think of him as her son if he were to embrace "Popery." It nearly broke Clarence's heart that the mother he loved so much could not accept his explanations. In her own heart, Maria held on to the dim hope that this visit home would be the means of Clarence's relenting and returning to his home, but it was not to be.

Reuben also could not believe his son was so swayed by these feelings. Always a religious man himself, he still could not believe Clarence would break so completely away and give up the world for a celibate life in a church structure so foreign to the

Walworths. Clarence knew that Reuben could never understand the fact that he, Clarence, had heard on one hand the call of God and on the other, the cry of flesh and blood, and he felt he must follow God, though his heart should break. He firmly believed the Catholic Church was the Christian fold into which Christ called his flock, even though it was often hated and misunderstood in America. He announced to his parents that his mind was firmly made up and he was leaving shortly to go to the Redemptorist Seminary in Belgium to begin his studies for the priesthood. At this utterance, Maria swooned and was carried off to her bed, in a spell of depression from which she never fully recovered. She barely left her bed after that. Reuben held her to his heart two years later as she faded away, heartbroken over the disappointment she felt in her son and unable to ever reconcile herself to his decision. When she died, Reuben knew a fire had been extinguished in his own heart that would never be rekindled.

Chapter Eight

❧

Reuben was roused from his long reveries by a shake on the shoulder from his new wife, Sarah, who told him he had been a million miles away for the last hour. The conductor had just come through the train to announce they would soon be arriving at Union Station in Washington.

When the train stopped, it was some minutes before the Hardin-Walworth family could alight and they were immediately caught up in the crush of people looking for porters. Finally, they were able to gather in the middle of the station and young Lemuel made sure he did not stray too far away from his mother and sister. This was the biggest crush of people and the most excitement he had ever seen and it left him with the feeling that Washington must be the most important place in the world.

Just then a darkly handsome and rather imposing man came striding through, and upon seeing them came rushing up to Reuben, grasping his hand and recalling their friendship from so long ago. Reuben proceeded to introduce Sarah, Mansfield, Ellen, and Lemuel to the stranger who turned out to be none other than the famous Whig statesman and orator, Daniel Webster, now serving as Secretary of State under President

Millard Fillmore. Webster acknowledged the introductions, paying special attention to Ellen, telling her she was sure to have a busy social schedule in Saratoga Springs when all the young men there met the pretty belle from the South. Ellen colored, but was pleased that her appearance provoked a favorable comment. She had never thought of herself as a beauty, but her features were regular, and she knew the styles that became her youthful figure. The young men had certainly seemed to find her attractive too, if her recent romances were any indication.

Webster reminisced with Reuben about the days when they had been working together in the north country of New York State, working to get the border question settled with Canada. He also joked about the times he had appeared in Reuben's courthouse in Saratoga and how he had been unsettled by Reuben's piercing questions and objections to his arguments in certain legal cases.

Then Webster turned to Sarah and told her he felt as if he already knew her, even though they had just met. He said he was a very good friend and strong supporter of Henry Clay and had even visited him at his lovely Kentucky home, Ashland, near Lexington. He also mentioned that Clay had been a good friend of Sarah's father, Horace Smith, who resided at Locust Grove in Louisville, and also that Clay often spoke of her first husband, the late Congressman from Illinois.

She was pleased by this recognition and said that although she had not seen Mr. Clay for some time, she hoped he would be present at the White House reception they had been invited to on the following day. Webster also was to be present at the reception, having just returned from a trip to South Carolina. He told Reuben how difficult it was being Secretary of State in these times when many Southerners were agitating to have their own way over their states' rights, and in the new territory with questions pro and con about slavery there. He knew too that he was not too popular among the Northerners, after being involved with the Compromise Law the year before. Still, he felt it was easier to try to appease the hot-headed Southerners than to fight them.

Saying goodbye to Webster, Reuben hurried the group through the doors of the station and they hailed a carriage to take them to the Willard Hotel, just a short way from the White House. The next day dawned almost before they were ready for it. Ellen felt a sense of portent as they walked beneath the porticoed entrance to the White House. She was overwhelmed, as only a young girl could be, to find herself entering the most important house in the nation. As she passed down the long corridor, she felt as if her feet were floating over the marble floors; the importance of the occasion lent a sense of dignity to her bearing. She noticed that even Mansfield and Lemuel seemed to be suitably impressed.

The group was escorted into the Green Room, where tea and refreshments would be served. A hush fell over the guests as President and Mrs. Fillmore entered and a military attaché directed Reuben and his family to a place in the receiving line. Reuben had a few moments to reflect on his own involvement in the political scene. He had long had ties to the Democrats, joining the Tammany Society while yet a law student in Troy. He had also become involved with the Bucktail politicos through his acquaintance with DeWitt Clinton, a renegade Republican. These Bucktails were a radical and less prosperous element of the Democratic Party who backed Van Buren and Governor Tompkins. In the 1840s, the disputes over slavery's extension into the new territories split the Democrats and embroiled Reuben in inter-party strife. Martin Van Buren, the son of a tavern keeper in the old Dutch village of Kinderhook, New York, was looming as a power on the political horizon. He led a group of Democrats who supported the Wilmot Proviso barring slaves from newly acquired Mexican territories (Texas). These free soil proponents were labeled Barn Burners, because of the likeness to a farmer burning his barn to get rid of rats. Another group of Democrats felt the Barn Burners endangered the Union by opposing slavery in Texas, and this group received the name of Hunkers.

The Barn Burners bolted from the national convention in 1848 and held their own separate convention in Utica, New York. Searching for a prominent man to lead their ticket they offered the nomination to Reuben Walworth, but he declined. He was against the agitation of the Anti-Slavery Movement in the North for he felt it defeated certain Southern attitudes that were in favor of a gradual system of emancipation and he felt that this was the only practical method of ending slavery. At the urging of John V. L. Pruyn, a prominent Albany lawyer, Reuben accepted the nomination of the Hunkers for the governorship of New York. However, the Whig Party carried both the state and nation because of the Democratic split.

The President circulated among his guests and eventually got to the circle where Reuben was standing chatting with some acquaintances. The President shook hands warmly with Reuben and recalled their school days at Union College and several law cases they had been mutually involved with back in the late 1820s. He jokingly recalled how he had been defeated in 1844 for the governorship of New York by Silas Wright, again with the major issue of the campaign revolving around the anti-slavery question, and Fillmore decried the fact that the same fate had been Reuben's in 1848. Reuben assured the President that his defeat in the race had quite soured him on politics and that he would never again run for public office, even though he was against slavery and free-soilism. He said he had hoped to be of some use to his country and state after the end of his Chancellorship, but politics was much too complicated at present because of the slavery issue. Reuben then led President Fillmore over to his little family group that was standing near the tea table, talking with Daniel Webster and Henry Clay about the merits of pasturing horses on the rich bluegrass of the fields around Lexington.

Chapter Nine

The trip from Washington to Saratoga was uneventful and seemed a pale aftermath to the excitement the group had experienced in Washington. Henry Taylor was waiting at the station in Saratoga to meet their train and as the carriage rolled north along Broadway, Ellen began to look about with interest. The street they were traveling was quite impressive, with spacious lawns surrounding large houses that had an air of elegance. Certainly people of taste and means must reside in these homes. The idea began to creep into her consciousness that perhaps Saratoga Springs was not as much a backwoods town as she had originally thought.

Of course, people did come here from all over the east coast to "take the waters" of its famous springs in search of a cure for their ailments, or just to provide a tonic for jaded spirits. Even many Southern families felt that their summer was not complete without a visit to Saratoga Springs during the season, and they tirelessly braved the long trek by train or boat to spend several weeks in the cool greenness of the little northern city. As early as 1830, the bottled waters of the Congress Spring were being touted as having great medicinal properties and were being shipped to customers in every part of the world. As she was absorbed in her musings, the carriage slowed to a halt before a long white fence, intercepted with sturdy short pillars that matched the corners of the house behind it. Reuben beamed with pride as he announced to his new family they had at long last arrived home.

The plain, low, old-fashioned dwelling sat amid a grove of tall rustling pine trees, its simple classical architecture blending into the landscape. On either side of the two-story central block were attached wings in perfect symmetry, with sheltering porches. The white paint and green shutters gave it a sparkling appearance and the harmonizing white-painted fence across the entire front of the property contributed to a sense of order and unity. It was not an overpowering mansion, but it had an impression of solidity and sheltering warmth that made Ellen feel at once she could be comfortable in this house.

The group alighted and with a quizzical expression, Mrs. Walworth hustled her children up the walk, eager to inspect her new home and begin life in this northern city, far removed from the rather languorous and servant-filled life she had led in Kentucky, and the socially exciting life she had found in Illinois and Washington as the wife of a lawyer, Congressman, and soldier.

As belongings were unpacked and trunks stowed in the attic, the family settled in, taking over bedrooms left vacant some years before by the marriages of the Chancellor's three daughters. Reuben's son, Clarence, was away, serving in a preaching missionary capacity in various parts of the country with the Redemptorist Order. It was only in March 1851 that Clarence had finally returned to America from his priestly studies, ordination, and subsequent parish duties in Europe. He had returned on a mission to America, to convert his countrymen, and had journeyed to Saratoga Springs in a contrite mood, appealing to the family's sense of love and his own filial devotion, to entreat them to accept him again as a family member in good standing, even though he was now long committed to his religious vocation. His father, after much soul-searching, and because he was basically a just man, had reconciled with the young priest. Thus, the door of the home would always again be open to receive him. Clarence's nature was warm and loving; he had felt great sorrow over brining unhappiness into the family group, but now all that was erased. In fact, at the Chancellor's death in 1867, he breathed his last in the arms of his beloved son, Father Clarence Walworth.

At the age of eighteen, Ellen was pliable and attempted to adjust to her new surroundings, even though some social snubs made her feel that the Yankees were often a conceited lot who belittled everything outside of their own sphere of influence. When Mansfield's chums stopped by to meet the new girl in town, she tried to be pleasant to them, but the Northern girls could not help showing their own ignorance of places far away. They made catty remarks in Ellen's hearing to the fact that they could not believe people in Illinois could dress so fashionably and that probably Ellen had had a complete wardrobe fitting in Washington so that the Chancellor would not be embarrassed by a bunch of country bumpkins coming in to fashionable Saratoga Springs.

The lump in Ellen's throat dissolved into hot temper and as she started to cross the room, Mansfield Walworth came to her side and tenderly put his arm about her waist, urging her to forget about the remarks as the girls were just showing jealousy. Mansfield also took her part by telling the girls that Ellen had had a fine education at the Female Academy and that there were lecturers, singers, pianists, works of art, and the plays of Shakespeare, even in the town of Jacksonville. Ellen also haughtily stated that social life was patterned after that of old Virginia and Kentucky where everyone had a command of good manners and that life values were not made in monied calculations, but in a whole world of sentiment.

Ellen tried to ignore other little barbs that might be thrown her way at parties and social gatherings, and she did make many new acquaintances, but she would not call them friends. None could ever take the place of her dearest friend, Mary Duncan of Illinois. The first few months in Saratoga found her still longing for the old days, and she and Mary exchanged letters at a rapid rate. "This city is more beautiful than I had imagined. There are may delightful walks and rides in the surrounding countryside. But how I miss the intelligent, simple and refined society in the West. Saratoga is an ostentatious place, decidedly Yankee, with a conceited and selfish society. I really detest Northerners, excepting of course, my dear new brother, Mansfield, who is a very good friend to me." So ran many of her letters to both Mary Duncan and Libby Eddy. Again in 1851, she wrote to Mary that she "wanted to go to the Empire City and hear Jenny Lind in concert. But she wanted Mansfield to go along also as "the old folks are taken up with themselves, and I will be lonely and mad all the time if he doesn't go."

Ellen demonstrated her independent spirit one morning by coming downstairs and startling everyone at the breakfast table with her costume—a pair of navy blue bloomers topped with a short navy blue dress. Her mother was shocked and immediately forbade her to be seen in such an outlandish dress. Ellen tried to sooth her mother's feelings by saying that these were fashionable and so much more comfortable and adaptable than long skirts. Mansfield quickly came to her defense, saying that he would be only too happy to escort Ellen to the park to take the

waters at the Columbian Spring as soon as breakfast was finished. Sarah announced they would do no such thing. However,
this was only one of the series of episodes in the lives of the two
young people that drew them closer and closer together. Ellen
found a congenial spirit in Mansfield, and together they shared a
new-found friendship that ripened into real love.

The bloomer episode prompted another letter to Mary
Duncan. "Well, the boys like my bloomers anyway, even if
Mother doesn't. When I have them on Mansfield pulls down my
hair and chases me about the yard. I am getting to be a real
tomboy. I feel so free and natural when I am wearing them. I can
jump, skip rope, swing and play games. Jut try wearing them
once, Mary, and you will never want to wear long dresses again."

In another letter she wrote, "There is no young person in this
house except Mansfield. I should be dreadfully lonely without
him. He enjoys all that is good and beautiful." And again, "I look
for all my happiness at home. It makes little difference whether I
like Saratoga people or not for I have not found another congenial spirit since I left Jacksonville, but Mansfield contributes to the
largest portion of my happiness. He at least is free of all
Yankeeism and he does have the power of winning ladies'
hearts."

By this time, her brothers, Martin and Lemuel Hardin had
gone off to the fall term of a boarding school in nearby Ballston
Spa, so Ellen and Mansfield were often quite unchaperoned in
the house. The parents were busy with their own activities and
absorbed in their new love. This lack of parental attention only
motivated the young people's need for each other's company.

Chapter Ten

ᴗᴥᴗ

One afternoon, sometime after the family group had arrived at home, the door opened to Father Clarence, come to meet his new relatives and spend a few days of leave at home. He was made welcome and after dinner was plied with questions concerning his work and travels. He charmed everyone with his warm and sincere character and quite bedazzled the precocious Ellen with his tales of travel at home and abroad. While he was not as handsome as Mansfield, he had a special aura. The very room was full of his presence; his missionary zeal could not help but be exercised, even on the members of his own family. When he left them a few days later, even his new stepmother was urging him to come back again soon. His stepbrother, Martin Hardin, pressed his hand with a friendly grip that ensured a future welcome. As he went down the walk to the visiting carriage, Martin could not help thinking that there was something about Father Clarence that set one thinking about one's own religious faith and reexamining the meaning of one's life. This was the beginning of many visits by Father Clarence, and he was always eagerly awaited and warmly welcomed into the family circle.

As 1851 drew to a close, the Chancellor was busy at his law office and active in civic affairs. When he had moved to Pine Grove, he and his first wife had taken great delight in setting up his courtroom in the north wing of the house. It was just inside the main entrance and three steps down from the front hall. Almost austere in appearance, it held the Judge's high-legged, slant-topped desk and stool on a platform that was raised about a foot. There was a long table in the center upon which the lawyers could spread their papers. Along the wall were strong chairs with writing arms and in cool weather, there was always a cheery blaze in the fireplace.

Over the years, there had been little change in the room's appearance. Something about the room reflected the Judge's personality, for he was known throughout law circles for his keen mind and his biting sarcasm that had earned him the nickname of "Rawhide." He frequently interrupted the speaker before his bench in a rather abrupt manner, but he never forgot his modest origins, and in his little courtroom he uttered decrees that gave him judicial immortality.

That talent had never been able to reach its fullest potential in ways that would serve the country that Reuben loved so well. In 1843, Reuben's name was placed in nomination by President Tyler for the office of Justice of the Supreme Court of the United States, but because of opposition of several senators, Henry Clay among them, his name was withdrawn, and Samuel Nelson was nominated in his place. There was considerable speculation that one of the reasons Reuben lost the nomination was because of a judgment he once made in the case of a fugitive slave from Louisiana named Jack. Reuben did order that the slave be returned to his mistress, upholding a New York Supreme Court decision. However, in a separate opinion, he denied congressional power to legislate on the escape of slaves from one state to another, and he upheld the constitutional rights of slaves as native-born citizens. These opinions were considered hostile to the interests of slaveholders, one of whom was Henry Clay of Kentucky.

During the 1840s also, Reuben's Chancery Court had come under fire because it was felt the caseload was becoming too much for one man to carry, and also that too much power was vested in one person. The state constitutional convention of 1846 upheld sweeping reforms in the judiciary, and the Chancery post was abolished and Reuben's courtroom closed in July of 1848. Nevertheless, everyone continued to call him Chancellor until the day he died.

One day shortly after Clarence's visit, Sarah Walworth took Ellen aside to confide to her that she was pregnant with the Chancellor's child. Although she had carried out the duties of the marriage bed, she had supposed herself too old to conceive. However, as the situation now stood, she would need Ellen to be of some help to her and lend her strength in this ordeal.

Swallowing a big lump that had seemed suddenly to be lodged near the middle of her throat, Ellen could not help but answer in a strangled voice that she was shocked and disappointed that this had happened. She felt it would cause a lot of bad feeling in the Chancellor's family with his becoming a father again at the age of sixty-three. However, in the next breath she did assure her mother that she would help out wherever necessary and with that statement escaped from the room as quickly as possible. She felt slightly nauseated and her confidence was badly shaken. At once she decided she must seek out Mansfield and confide this startling news to him. It was not long before she found him and they disappeared behind closed doors into the library. Ellen poured out on his shoulder all her revulsion at the thought of her mother's pregnancy. But when the tirade was ended, she was suddenly struck by the thought that something fatal could also happen to her mother in these circumstances and then she and her brothers would be parentless. With that thought, a new rash of tears flooded over Mansfield's sympathetic shoulder. However, it was not long before warm caresses and the "perfect sunshine" of Mansfield's smile dried up the tears and Ellen accepted with more composure the irrefutable facts of life.

Chapter Eleven

F ather Clarence came often to visit when he could take time from his missionary duties. In spite of himself he could not suppress the zeal which he had for the propagation of his Faith, even though he knew of his father's aversion to that religion and the stubbornness that Reuben displayed in adhering to his Presbyterian tenets. However, the group from Kentucky was beginning to ask him leading questions and rely on him for guidance and advice. Even though Sarah now accompanied her husband to the Presbyterian church in Saratoga Springs, her Episcopalian background in Kentucky and Illinois gave her a familiarity with Clarence's beliefs. Ellen and Martin were at an impressionable age; the influence of Clarence was not lost on them. They enjoyed his company, respected his views, and felt him to be an honest and sincere young man who was truly marching to Zion in an exemplary fashion. Since Mansfield doted on whatever pleased Ellen, it was not long before his thinking too came to take on the colorations of his step-relatives. Father Clarence was his own brother, and the tie that binds had an even stronger pull. Mansfield had always felt that Clarence was far wiser than he, and he had always reluctantly admired the traits of perseverance and congeniality in Clarence that he, Mansfield, sadly lacked.

He confided to Ellen that he felt Clarence really had something very worthwhile in his work in the Church and that it was a tremendous challenge to seek out lost souls and save them for eternal life. He, Mansfield, was not enamored of a career in law, even though his father kept trying to cram it down his throat. He felt perhaps he should talk with Clarence and see what he would think about Mansfield's entering the seminary. He cautioned Ellen not to say a word to her mother or his father, because the roof might blow off the house if they knew what he was considering.

A cloud of fear swept over Ellen as she heard Mansfield uttering these thoughts. Whatever would she do in this city if he were to go away and leave her all alone with the old folks? Her heart would surely break if he were to shut himself away in some seminary. She urged him to consider this course of action very wisely for it would be a tremendous rejection of so many of the things that pleased him most. If Mansfield were to enter the priesthood, her almost constant companion would be gone. At the mere suggestion that she might lose him she suddenly realized that her feelings for him were becoming more intense with each passing day.

Ellen did confide to Mansfield, however, that she too had been much taken with what she had been reading and learning about the Catholic religion. She even swore him to secrecy in the fact that she was thinking of someday joining the Roman Catholic Church herself. She asked Mansfield to consider joining her in that step before he went through with anything so final as really becoming a seminarian. She also told him that her mother had already been suspecting from all of her reading and discussions that she, Ellen, had come under Clarence's influence. She said her mother had told her that if Ellen had any thoughts of converting, it would be to her, Sarah's, everlasting displeasure.

Since Mansfield could never keep anything secret for very long, it was not too many days before everyone in the household heard him declare that he was actively considering a career in the Church and had spoken with Clarence about the possibility of becoming a priest. In the greatest agitation at hearing these disclosures, Reuben hastily retreated to his desk and penned a long letter to Clarence: "I understand from your brother that he has spoken to you concerning the matter of his embracing Catholicism and entering the priesthood. You know it has always been in my mind that he should pursue a career in law instead, so that he might be of some assistance to me in my practice, or otherwise start a new practice of his own.

If he continues in this scheme of embracing a religious vocation, there is no way that he shall receive a cent of money from me to finance his plans. I will never believe that the priesthood is his proper vocation. Mansfield has so far in life been nothing but a spoiled wastrel. He has never earned any money, and because of that he cannot know the value of or be trusted with money. He is an idler and will not try to be anything else. Please use whatever influences you can bring to bear to change his course of action."

It was not only Reuben who was upset about the prospect of Catholicism again rearing its head in his family circle. In February of 1852, Ellen received a letter from her brother Martin, written from his boarding school in Ballston spa: "Ellen, I am uneasy about a recent letter I had from Mother. She says you have been reading many books about the Catholic religion. She feels you have almost persuaded yourself that it is a better Faith than that of your parents. Your friends, Mother and other relatives are much opposed to that religion. Ask many questions and turn your mind much on this subject. Last, but not least, listen to the advice of your mother."

When the Chancellor's two older daughters heard from their father of Mansfield's vacillations with religion, they both wrote him letters of advice and alarm that only made him more angry and vindictive. Mary E. Jenkins was the widow of a New York businessman; Ann Eliza Backus was the wife of Jonathan T. Backus, pastor of the First Presbyterian Church in Schenectady. Even though they lived not far from Saratoga, their own family life and long absence from the immediate Saratoga scene made them infrequent visitors to the new family ensconced in the family homestead.

Shortly thereafter, Sarah received a letter from some old friends in Washington, who extended an invitation for Ellen to come and stay with them for a month or two that winter. They promised to try to make her life with them enjoyable and they would be happy to see that she had a pleasant time on the social scene in the Capital. Sarah urged Ellen to accept because she clearly saw advantages to the girl in such an undertaking, even though she knew she would need Ellen's help back home when she delivered the new little Walworth baby in April.

After her bouts with the smug Yankees in Saratoga society, Ellen was pleased with this offer to get out of the provincial city and into a wider sphere in Washington. Even so, she doubted she would be completely happy without Mansfield. When she voiced this thought to Sarah it did not take long for her mother to reply tartly that it might be good for Ellen to make the acquaintance of some new and promising young men, since she did not think Mansfield showed much industry in anything. She also reminded Ellen that Mansfield had been the fastest young man in college and that Clarence did not think he should ever have attended Union, and that it was the ruination of him. However, since Eliphalet Nott, the president of that school, had been a good friend of Reuben's, he thought that since Clarence had graduated from Union, it would be a fine school for Mansfield.

Ellen, in turn, thought her mother was being too judgmental and she and the Chancellor did not understand the fine strain of feeling that ran through Manse. He had been trying to do some serious writing and Ellen saw in this a sign that he was going to settle down to some serious activity very soon. Besides, she could not help thinking that since he was so sweet and caring, it was no wonder he was a great beau.

Plans for the trip to Washington went forward and soon after Christmas Ellen found herself settled in a comfortable home with more invitations to parties and balls than she could attend. She did meet an attractive young lawyer with whom she had a happy interlude. She wrote long letters to Mansfield about her activities. It seemed as if she wanted him to know that at nineteen she was still a belle with the ability to attract young men just as much as he had the ability to attract young women. In fact, her letters to her dear friend, Mary Duncan in Illinois, so upset that young lady that she wrote to Ellen: "Beware—beware. Your last letter makes me fear 'tis not well between you and Mansfield. But as you say 'twill make no difference to him. He has done likewise to himself, so be it. Why do you not write me more about the time, if there be any, set for your wedding?"

When Ellen returned home, she was again strongly influenced by Mansfield's charming manner, and their companionship resumed. In February 1852, Clarence came to Albany on a preaching mission. She and Mansfield attended the service at St.

Joseph's Church in that city. A very large crowd of people had come to hear Father Clarence preach.

When the service was finished, the great organ played its majestic melodies, and the call was put forth for those touched by the preaching of the word to come forward to declare for the Faith. In a dramatic moment, Clarence climaxed his exhortations by grasping a huge black cross set up on the podium, imploring those to come forward who felt their hearts ready to accept the gospel message. Ellen rose dazedly from her seat, captured by the urgency of the moment, and walked up the aisle as a surge of religious fervor overcame her. She felt that in declaring for conversion she had found the answer to her religious questions of the past few years. Mansfield returned alone on the train that night to Saratoga while she went to the nearby Convent of the Sacred Heart to prepare for the sacraments that would make her a Catholic. In later life, she would define her decision as: "It opened a new world to me in which I entered upon and enjoyed a new spiritual and intellectual life."

Chapter Twelve

 ⁓

The new baby arrived in April, a year after Sarah's marriage to the Chancellor. She presented him with a son, Reuben H. Walworth, Jr., but the child only lived six months. In the midst of all this excitement over the new baby, Mansfield and Ellen felt a growing desire for each other, and being together constantly under the same roof, often unchaperoned because of their parent's social and business obligations, they realized that marriage was the only answer to their passion. Their love was genuine and their desire to be as one so great that they agreed to talk with Father Clarence about Mansfield's converting to the Catholic faith so that Clarence could marry them. They did much of their planning in secret as they were not yet ready to divulge their engagement to their parents. However, after a few weeks they could contain themselves no longer and astounded Reuben and Sarah by announcing they loved one another and planned to be married soon. Reuben received this announcement by the young people with surprise and consternation showing strongly on his face. He harshly reminded Mansfield that it was only a short time ago he had been contemplating the priesthood for a vocation. He certainly hoped that now Mansfield was more sincere in his declaration of love for Ellen.

Mansfield did not accept the reproach his father had given him and declared that Reuben of all people knew he was not cut out for life in the Church. He said when he really seriously started considering the situation, he realized he and Ellen were meant to be together and it was time to settle down, as Reuben was often fond of telling him. Sarah shot a glance at the radiant Ellen during this interchange and knew, with a cold feeling in her chest, that there would be no turning back now that the march to the altar had begun. But her heart and mind were full of reservations nevertheless.

Ellen stressed they wanted to be married very soon and that they had no plans for a large and impressive wedding. She announced that Father Clarence had been in on the planning and had agreed to marry them, since Mansfield was converting to Catholicism so they could be married at Saint Peter's Church in Saratoga Springs. With a thunderstruck look, Reuben quickly got up from the table and left the room and not long after, Sarah joined him. Mansfield went to Ellen and took her gently into his outstretched arms, telling her that although their parents seemed dumbstruck, now they could go on making their plans in the open. He passionately reiterated how much he loved and needed Ellen and gave her a long, lingering kiss.

In a letter to Mary Duncan a few days later, Ellen complained that although she and Mansfield wanted a small wedding ceremony, Reuben felt a large social gathering must be the order of the affair because of the prestige of the families and the many friends who would be offended if they were not invited to the wedding. Ellen urged Mary Duncan to come to the East and be her only bridesmaid.

Shortly before the marriage was to take place, Ellen got a brief glimpse of Mansfield's jealous moods when he accosted her with a letter that had come for her from Washington, written in a man's strong hand. The caustic tone of his voice made her heart skip a beat as he accused her of writing to someone she had met there the past winter, and doing so behind his back. Ellen tried to laugh off the incident with tales of her little flirtations that had been soon forgotten when she came home to Saratoga and Mansfield. She insisted Mansfield was the one who had always had her heart. He relented a bit and handed her the letter, but as she read it a blush suffused her face as she realized it was a proposal of marriage from one of the young men she had met.

On hearing this, Mansfield flew into another jealous rage, accusing Ellen of carrying on a clandestine affair but Ellen reminded Mansfield she had known this young man to be an honest, intelligent, young lawyer with position and influence, and a perfect gentleman. She told him he should realize she would not align herself with anyone less, and that now she would have to reply to the letter and tell the young man she was about to be married to Mansfield.

In a letter a few weeks later to Mary Duncan she confided: "I know in commencing life with one so young and inexperienced as Manse I shall have to take upon myself part of the burden, and I can now see very plainly, trials and difficulties to encounter."

The wedding on July 29, 1852, was a highlight of the Saratoga social scene and within a few months Ellen had good news to report to Mansfield, something that she felt would make him even more loving and happy. In the privacy of their room she told him she was sure they were going to have a baby and would soon confirm it by a visit to the doctor. Mansfield's reaction was predictable and he was overcome with emotion at this joyous news, but then he drew back, assuring her that he could not bear it if anything should happen to Ellen—that no baby could ever take her place in his heart.

But Ellen's pregnancy did not go as smoothly as she had hoped and she was confined to her room for two months. This only increased Mansfield's tenderness and attention. At her first trip outside the bedroom, he picked her up in his arms and carried her down the stairs. The love and devotion the couple felt for each other seemed to be increased by this new anticipation they felt in their lives.

Chapter Thirteen

᪥

One day in March of 1853, Sarah remarked that since Ellen's condition seemed much improved, and Reuben had to take a journey to Philadelphia and Washington on business, she would like to accompany him. She hoped to visit old friends and also to entertain influential people in Washington. Since her son, Martin Hardin, had high hopes of entering the United States Military Academy at West Point, Sarah felt it would be useful to make all the contacts possible with those people who could influence his nomination. She also felt she should travel on to Kentucky to see her father, who was becoming elderly and enfeebled. Always the dutiful mother, Sarah went off to Washington to push for Martin's interest, and she also made an extended visit to Kentucky, not returning home until early May. Later that same month, she and Reuben went on a trip to New York City.

Ellen felt very confined to the house in the fine, early days of spring, as Mansfield did not want her to go out walking on the streets of Saratoga because he did not want anyone to see her in her pregnant condition. He raised a fuss even about her brothers seeing her in that condition when they came home from boarding school but, after all, there was not much he could do about that. However, he insisted she stay in the house with him, as he was busy with the "Spike" case. Since he was his father's law clerk, this case had kept him very busy doing a lot of legal work he did not particularly enjoy.

The Spike case involved Henry Burden of Troy and his having the rights to a patent on an improved hook-headed railroad spike. The Burden Iron Works expected to manufacture and make a lot of money on the sale of this spike. However, it seemed that the Corning Iron Works in Albany copied the same kind of spike and sold hundreds of thousands of them across the country. Burden was angered because he believed that Erastus Corning had infringed upon his patent rights in an underhanded manner, so he instituted suit. The U.S. Supreme Court ruled in Burden's favor, but the assessment of damages, which ran into an extremely large sum of money, was referred to Reuben Walworth as Chancellor for adjudication.

The case revolved over the question of how many spikes Corning made, how many were sold, and for how much money. Also the question of how many spikes Burden could have made and sold if Corning had not infringed upon the patent. William Seward, Reuben's longtime friend, was one of many lawyers involved in the case and it was to take a long period of time to get the entire matter sorted out. Mansfield complained to Ellen that Reuben had him doing the lion's share of the work and so he would have very little time to give to her or to anything else at the moment. He fretted that he could not give time to the writing of novels, a new passion with him that took up much of his spare time.

Ellen had plenty of time on her hands and so she wrote a letter to Mary Duncan to see if she could come to Saratoga and pay a visit in the summer. She noted that Mary had been postponing a trip East much too long and that one would never know how much she, Ellen, had missed her oldest and dearest friend the long months they had been separated. She invited Mary to come and stay for an extended visit and comfort her old friend who was in such physical and mental distress. Mary accepted the invitation and came East just before the birth of Ellen and Mansfield's first child, Francis Hardin Walworth, on August 17, 1853.

Reuben was away on business in Springfield, Massachusetts, when his first grandchild was born. Sarah wrote him a long letter about the birth and he replied in kind, telling of his joy in the arrival of this newest addition to the Walworth family. The sentences of the letter resounded with increased love and affection for his wife and stepdaughter also. In another letter to Mansfield, his words contained only a thinly veiled suggestion that he get on with his law studies so he could support his increased family, but there was no hint of congratulation to Mansfield.

So happy was Ellen with the shared life with Mansfield in these early years of their marriage that it occasioned her to write to a friend: "I sometimes tremble at the thought of my present happiness, fearing it cannot last, because of such a world of sorrows and changes." This tranquil period in her life was reflected in her happy expression. She had a sleek center part to her hair, with puffs over the ears, and its length braided over the top of her head. Her wide set eyes, with a droop to the lids, gave her a languorous look that was becoming and stirred feelings of love in the heart of Mansfield. This period, too, was a tranquil one for the sometimes volatile Mansfield as he relished his new fatherhood and enjoyed playing with the baby. However, he often complained that the baby took too much of Ellen's time away from him, especially when he was free of work and spent the evenings at home with her. He seemed possessed to be with Ellen at each free minute, and he needed her love and approval constantly to keep him reassured of his own self worth. His ego was immensely boosted in 1853, when his first book "Mission of Death" was published. Its sales sent confidence soaring in Mansfield that his writing was of some real worth.

Nevertheless, the couple continued to reside in their parent's home. Mansfield often felt stifled under the constant prodding of his father to keep at his legal work with the long, drawn-out Spike case. By 1855, Ellen expressed in a letter to a friend a desire to move back to the West and leave her parents' home. She implied this would happen after the settling of the Spike case, but the suit dragged on and on and the idea faded. After eight years in Saratoga Springs she had begun to be fond of the place and probably realized that the West of her childhood would be so changed that it would be a sorrow to go back. In the winter of 1855, she and Mansfield accompanied Sarah and Reuben on a business trip to Washington, D.C., but Ellen, now in her second pregnancy, became ill and returned home early with little Frank.

Mansfield often spent a large part of his evenings reading and making elaborate notes for literary ventures that he seldom talked about with anyone, including Ellen. As time went on, he spent long hours in their room, writing with a fervor he did not give to his legal career. Ellen said nothing, believing that perhaps a latent talent would prove to be both economically and socially productive, and she was often glad for the respite it gave her from some of Mansfield's increasing petulance.

She had tried to interest him in the social life of the little city and in acquiring a circle of friends with whom they could dine and play cards. They did attempt more social life for a time, but Mansfield's sense of superiority over all who came, and his churlish manner if everything did not proceed as he wished it to, turned even these people of his own social stature to offering excuses when invited to share his company. Ellen tried to attribute Mansfield's occasional outbursts to the vagaries of an artistic talent. However, she was still enamored of his physical charms and the time when he could be a loving and compassionate husband. Their moments of loving intimacy produced a second child, a son, and a third, a daughter, born within the next five years. Both children died in infancy.

After these events, Mansfield would shut himself away for days and be in such a mood of depression that there was no way of reaching him. Ellen would take dinner to his room, but he only opened the door to receive the food and then it was quickly shut and locked. She pleaded with him to let her in to comfort him, but there would be only silence for an answer. Finally, at the end of these morose periods, he would come to her and cry in her arms over his failure as a husband and his inability to provide her with the living children they both desired.

Ellen tried to soothe him as much as possible by pleading with him not to blame himself and to accept the fact that God's will must be done. She reminded him again and again how fortunate they were to have little Frank and their loving family members around them and that they were young and could have more children in time. Eventually her calm reasoning would soothe the volcanic feelings of Mansfield and turn them into a passionate vein that ended up in an intimate interval in the bedroom.

Chapter Fourteen

The months and years slipped by as the threads of life were woven by the family at Pine Grove. In the spring of 1858, yet another crisis reared its head in the form of a telegram that came to Reuben, informing him that his son, Clarence, was ill with "brain fever" in New York City at the Paulist headquarters.

Reuben, immediately upon hearing this news, hastened to pack his valise and took the next train from Saratoga to be with his son and make sure that everything possible was being done for him. He told Sarah that as soon as Clarence was able to travel, he would bring him home to Pine Grove where he could make a complete recovery. Reuben could not help but feel that all the ardent preaching and arduous travel about the country had apparently completely exhausted Clarence and broken his health.

Within a few weeks, Clarence and his father were able to make the journey northward and the convalescence at home, coupled with plenty of rest in the fresh mountain air and wholesome food, soon restored Clarence to good health, but it was felt he should give up the grueling missionary work. He decided to separate from the Paulist Order, which he had helped found, and in the summer of 1858 he accepted a pastorate at Saint Peter's Church in Troy, New York.

Ellen also had news for the family that spring. She was again pregnant and the baby would be born near the end of September. She was praying that everything would be all right this time for she did not believe that Mansfield could keep his sanity if they lost another child.

This new baby was a girl, born on October 2, and Mansfield insisted upon naming her Ellen H. Walworth. This might have been done to assuage the guilt he was beginning to feel over his inability to control his temper, not only with Ellen, but with everyone else. He felt out of sorts with life in general, and in trying to compensate for certain shortcomings, he adopted a new pose. He had always strongly admired the lifestyle of the landed aristocrats and tried in all his doings to dress and act like that class. He became known about the streets of Saratoga Springs as a "fashion plate," with admirably hand-tailored suits and Panama hats. While it was necessary for him to keep working at his law practice for financial security, he resented the time it took away from his writings, and this also did nothing to improve his disposition. While he also desired children, he resented the demands they made on his time alone with Ellen. His smart appearance on the street contrasted sharply with his insolent manners at home.

Martin Hardin was at the United States Military Academy and Ellen's brother Lemuel had gone to Kentucky for an extended visit with relatives. However, the small children running about the house and the presence of his parents made for a certain amount of confusion and this was wearing upon Mansfield's equilibrium. He complained constantly that he could not settle down to serious writing with all the daily interruptions and that he desperately needed peace and quiet for himself.

Hearing these daily tirades wore on Ellen's nerves and she could not always contain her own feelings and often found herself impatient. She could not help but remind Mansfield that she too was stuck in an endless round of responsibilities for the children and often felt quite unwell because of her frequent pregnancies. She also could not help but notice that Mansfield's work and his shutting himself in his room to write books for hours on end left him no time at all for companionship with her. She had begun by this time to have a secret longing to develop her own intellect instead of always being tied down with mundane daily tasks that offered no mental stimulation. However, when she tried to explain this position to Mansfield, he always countered with the objection that a woman's first and foremost job was to take care of home and family and that she had asked for just that when she married him.

Reuben could not help being aware of and upset by these many outbursts and he talked with Ellen about it, saying that he could not help noticing the prolonged absences of Mansfield from the family circle. He hoped with all his heart that Mansfield was not forgetting the good things he had in such a lovely wife and children. He did think Mansfield really loved Ellen and the children very much, but he had always had an erratic streak in his nature. Reuben felt he should have realized this long ago, but he supposed he was so busy with his own law career and family and social responsibilities that he did not pay enough attention to Mansfield's problems.

Ellen appreciated Reuben's concerns and agreed that Mansfield was very emotional, but that quality also made him a warm and loving husband. In fact, she was sure he would be thrilled when she told him that even though little Nelly was only a few months old, she was already expecting another child. Even this good news did nothing to alter Mansfield's temperamental outbursts, however, and five weeks before Ellen's delivery, he suddenly announced to her he was leaving Saratoga to go to New York City where he could be by himself and settle down to serious writing. He announced he was finished with the practice of law and would be more than happy to leave the association with his father, since that man was impatient with Mansfield's actions, especially his drinking habits of late. He reminded Ellen that his father was very sanctimonious about the fact that he never touched anything but water to his lips. He also accused Ellen of being hypocritical about her faults and putting on a front of being sweet and pious and charming. He said she did not care about him, but only was thinking of her children and her charity organizations.

She, in her, turn could not believe he would do such a thing as leave just before her confinement. She had not had an inkling that he was planning such a drastic step. She could only ask herself in agonizing sorrow whatever had become of the wonderful times they used to have together, when they were so happy and so in love. Something had changed radically along the way for both herself and Mansfield.

All of the arguments, pleadings, and tears could not change Mansfield's mind and the next train took him away to New York and a rented room where he immersed himself in his manuscripts. For her part, Ellen's heart was heavy with the knowledge that their love was somehow tarnished and their relationship not what it had been just a few short years ago. A guilty feeling persisted that perhaps she had not been as responsive to his needs as she might have been. But she reasoned too that Manse's impatient behavior and his constant sarcasm made it very difficult to be as loving and understanding as she perhaps should be. She felt it was a good thing she would not be going out much for the next five weeks because of her condition. She hoped no one would suspect there was anything unusual in Mansfield's action because they would not hear of it.

Within a few days, she received a note from him stating he had taken a room in a brownstone house on Eighty Ninth Street in New York City. He told her he was taking long walks and savoring the varieties of big city life. He was also spending long hours filling sheets of paper with his imaginings. Somewhere in time, the couple had turned away from each other as comrades often do—even though the course was to prove especially fatal for them. Perhaps their differences were too great. Ellen was pious and conscientious, Mansfield a dreamer and a wastrel, and thus, a barrier had grown up between them.

Chapter Fifteen

⊙⊘

M ansfield continued his erratic comings and goings back and forth from New York City. Even with all this, and Ellen's hard work taking care of a growing family, the time went swiftly. On a late October day in 1859, Ellen was delivered of another baby daughter, named Clara Teresa. At once, a telegram was sent off to inform Mansfield of the news. Within a few hours of its receipt, the front door opened to an abashed Mansfield, who swiftly dropped his valise and ran up the stairs. Bursting through the door, he dropped to his knees beside the bed and gathered her in his embrace. He held her closely as tears rolled down his cheeks and he begged her forgiveness for not being there with her in her time of need. He said the telegram had struck him a terrible blow and suddenly he had seen how selfish he had been all along. He reassured her that he loved her as much as ever and begged her forgiveness for his acting such a cad.

The next two years sped by quickly, if not smoothly, with still more outbursts from the volcanic Mansfield when he was in town and much quiet thought by Ellen. The Victorian society of their time glorified the mother image, and Ellen was one of its finest proponents. However, by 1859, she was becoming much more pragmatic, after five pregnancies in six years, many times alone and without the comfort of a sustaining husband. True, when Mansfield was around he relished his fatherhood, but he could retire from it for months at a time, to devote endless hours to his writing. When she found herself pregnant in the fall of 1860, he seem delighted with the news at first, but soon entered into a period of morose and frustration.

Matters within the household were not going smoothly, either. The children were taking an increasing share of Ellen's time and attention. Sarah, herself first and foremost the epitome of the Victorian wife and mother, was now often away from Saratoga, visiting relatives in Kentucky or friends in Washington, and doing what she could in a social way to further the interests of her two sons. Reuben was often lonesome for her companionship, but he kept himself busy with his legal work and the many temperance and church activitities that had been his interest over the years.

Ellen was beginning to take a consuming interest in the mission work of the Catholic Church. She was spurred on by her natural devotion to worthy causes and by Father Clarence's influence when they were together. She had long been interested in Clarence's travels throughout the country, preaching and attempting to convert those who either had no faith or had lost it somewhere along the way. His work among the Indians of the American West and visits to their reservations were a constant source of interest to the inhabitants of Pine Grove. They were stirred to assist in their own small way by the stories that Father Clarence brought back, telling of the hardships of these forgotten people. Even when his health determined that he must give up the constant traveling and the rigorous schedule of a mission preacher, his experiences with these people led him to work for their betterment throughout his lifetime.

Ellen spent long hours with Clarence when he came home to Saratoga. She was seeking to understand and find a deep meaning in the religious tenets taught by the church. Her family problems led her to strive to gain inner peace and serenity through prayer and the reading of religious tracts, hoping to relieve the turmoil of conflicting feelings battering her mind and heart. Clarence represented a kindly tower of strength to the family members, and his visits were welcomed, especially by the female members of the household. Reuben, too, had mellowed over the years, and he thoroughly enjoyed hearing Clarence relate his experiences in the mission field, and took pleasure in the company of this many-faceted personality.

Although Reuben could never embrace the religious views that Clarence personified, still he felt a kindred spirit with his elder son. Indeed, they were very much alike in their kindliness of spirit and dignified manner of bearing. Clarence, having once practiced law, had never completely lost his feeling for the profession, but took an active interest in the affairs of state, often writing treatises on some question of national policy for religious journals or the press. He was a very versatile person who was completely at ease with many people and situations; this added to his air of competence. His father loved him as a son and respected his judgment as a man. This became all too apparent to Mansfield and further served to alienate him from the family circle.

In the fall of 1860, the household at Pine Grove was electrified when Abraham Lincoln received the Republican nomination for President of the United States, defeating Reuben's old friend and Union College associate, William H. Seward, on the third ballot. In speaking with Sarah about the turn of events, Reuben said he was sorry to see Seward lose the nomination because he was a brilliant man but he could not think of a finer, more humane man to be President than Lincoln when the country was in such turmoil. Reuben even declared that since Lincoln was the husband of Sarah's cousin, Mary Todd, he might even overturn his Democratic ideals and cast a vote for Lincoln. He did hope that if Abe was elected he would give Seward a cabinet post because the nation should not lose the abilities of a man of that stature. Sarah, on her part, thought it was certainly exciting to think that a close friend and relative of her own family might become President of the country. She was sure Mary Todd would be very pleased with this honor for her husband as she had constantly shared a passionate interest with him in politics and spurred him on day and night.

Reuben cautioned that if Lincoln won he would have a big job laid upon his shoulders for all the honor in the world could not compensate for the troubles he would have to endure if the nation kept heading in the direction it seemed to be going. The South would never accept a Republican victory, particularly because they hated the violent Abolitionists within the party. Such a victory would only make the South more intent upon a secession movement, which they had been threatening for too long. Reuben had always felt, as Lincoln did, that the government should be conciliatory and support non-interference with the Southern question of states rights and slavery, but time was running out and the Abolitionists were the incendiaries who had been trying for years to light the fires of a civil war.

By the time of Lincoln's inaugural in March of 1861, seven Southern states had announced their secession from the Union, and the Confederate government was already organized.

Nevertheless, Mrs. Lincoln and the party had planned an impressive inaugural ball and festivities, and Sarah Walworth was among the invited guests. She and Reuben went to Washington for the party, but Reuben shortly after, returned home to Saratoga Springs. Thoroughly enjoying the prominence her relatives gave to her situation, Sarah stayed on in Washington for a few more weeks to enjoy the round of social festivities with her first husband's cousin, the new First Lady of the nation, Mary Todd Lincoln. She received a letter from Reuben reading: "Invite Mrs. Lincoln for a friendly visit in June or July. She will, by that time, get tired of the routine of official visits." However, before Sarah returned to Saratoga the war had intervened and Sarah stayed on, exhilarated by the excitement of the wartime capital. In a letter to Ellen she said: "We are living history here now. I would not be anywhere else in the world."

His wife's prolonged absence caused Reuben to write urgently to Sarah: "I do wish that you would return at once to our home in Saratoga. I would feel much better if you were back here in your own home. With this war, there may be trouble very near Washington; then it might be impossible for you to get out without difficulty. I am distressed at your prolonged absence. I know how much you relish the social life in the Capital and that you are also eager to influence those who can advance Martin's army career, but I do miss your presence. If you so desire, I shall write to Abe Lincoln myself to ask that he do whatever he can personally to secure an agreeable situation for Martin."

The letters were written; the influence was spread about in Washington. In May 1861, Martin Hardin was commissioned a first lieutenant in the army of the United States.

Chapter Sixteen

O ne morning as Ellen passed the window in the parlor she
noticed the boy from the telegraph office coming up the
front walk. A feeling of dread passed through her as it always did
when this happened and she hoped that nothing was wrong with
Martin or her mother in Washington. She went into the front hall
and opened the door to the delivery boy with a feeling of anticipation, overshadowed with dread.

Since the telegram was addressed to Judge Walworth, she
immediately took it to Reuben in his courtroom office where he
was bent over the long table, working on a sheaf of papers spread
along its length. He opened the envelope quickly, also expecting
bad news, but presently a smile spread over his face as he told
Ellen the telegram was from the Secretary of State, Bill Seward.
Seward wanted Reuben to come to Washington and confer on
some ideas that he wanted to propose to President Lincoln, and
he felt he needed the advice of several legal minds. Reuben felt
the problem must be the question over the furor the government
was in with the Southern statesmen and their threats of secession. Seward had been one of the most powerful spokesmen for
resisting the spread of slavery. Having been the Governor of

New York and then Senator, he had plenty of political experience. Reuben could not help but remark that it had been a shame Seward did not receive the nomination for President in 1860, but he felt it was because there were too many political foes against him. He was glad though that Lincoln saw the good in Seward and made him his Secretary of State.

At once, Reuben put away his own work and began packing his valise for the trip to Washington with a feeling of anticipation. In putting aside his papers, Reuben knew it would take him longer to catch up with his workload when he got back home. It seemed to be taking him longer these days to keep up with his caseload, and he attributed it to getting along in years, although he did not like to admit to it. He did feel happy though that he would now be able to see his wife in Washington and he told Ellen he would give her love to both her mother and her brother Martin. All of the family were proud that Martin had graduated from the Military Academy and was now an officer in the U.S. Army.

After a tedious train journey, Reuben arrived in Washington and immediately walked to Sarah's boarding house. The next morning, he appeared at Secretary Seward's office and was warmly greeted by his old friend. Soon the Secretary, Reuben, and several other advisors were closeted in an adjoining meeting room, going over the details of a plan that Seward wanted to propose to President Lincoln, as a means of averting what now looked like a national catastrophe that would end in civil war.

Seward reminded the men that the South was still bucking the Compromise of 1850 and trying to get more territory into the Union as slave states rather than free and that they were also still ranting over nullification of the laws of Congress. He also reminded them that if these Southern states were allowed to declare unconstitutional any law Congress passed that did not suit the states' purposes, there would be no law at all and the states would be making all the decisions. He strongly felt the hot-headed Secessionists wanted to throw out the Union, and that very temper was driving the country to the brink of war. He again reiterated that the division of the Union would be a tragedy that would leave us vulnerable to all kinds of outside interference of other powers.

What Seward proposed to the men to meet this head-on collision was radical, but he threw it in as a last hope to avert catastrophe. Everyone knew that France and Spain had been trying to exert their influence into places where they had no right to be in the Caribbean, and that was getting pretty close to U.S. territory in Florida. Seward felt we should fling down the gauntlet and demand an explanation of their actions. Since he did not think they could come up with an answer that would be acceptable to our government, we would have the perfect excuse to declare war on them and that provoking a war with a country outside our borders could not help but reunite the people of the United States. He felt the South would be quick to answer a call to arms and join forces with the North against a common aggressor. The Southerners would like to see those Spanish colonies of Puerto Rico and Cuba come into the Union as slave territories. He added that if we won the war, we would obtain some island bases in the Caribbean that would make good outposts for our fleet to control and give our shores added security.

When it came Reuben's turn to speak on this matter, he thoughtfully advised against trying to provoke war with a foreign power, even if these powers were not as strong as they once were. He felt it would tax the strength of the navy to its very limit and we would be taking on a task that might prove too large for us. The men met in heated session for two days and there was much debate and many suggestions put forth concerning the scheme. The final decision was for Seward to present the plan to the President for his consideration. After thoughtful deliberation of the plan, Lincoln gracefully but firmly, turned down Seward's proposal.

Before leaving Washington for home, Reuben paid a brief visit to his stepson, Martin D. Hardin, at his army post near the city. Reuben could not help but notice the activity at the post and the increased security measures that were being taken with visitors. Train and wagonloads of freight, much of it ammunition and ordinance supplies, was being stacked in warehouses that had been hastily constructed. Martin did little to reassure his stepfather as to the purpose of all this activity. But he hastened to caution Reuben not to say anything about all this activity to his mother or Ellen. There was no sense in causing them needless worry at this time when perhaps it might prove to be a false alarm that military activity would be initiated against an enemy.

The two men discussed in earnest the national situation and the intensity of feelings in both the North and South. Martin could not imagine having to shoot at someone who was a friend or a relative, especially since his own heritage was Southern. He knew that for himself he would stay with the U.S. Army but he could not help thinking of Lemuel and what path he might choose, for he felt Lemuel's sympathies were with the South.

Reuben knew what Martin was saying was all too true and he left the young man with a heavy heart as he contemplated what the future would bring. As a staunch Northerner, he agreed with President Lincoln that the Union must be preserved at any price, yet his wife and stepchildren were of Southern background. Indeed, his own son Mansfield had been joined to them by his marriage to Ellen. What would be their sentiments if an actual conflict ensued? What sort of pains and pressure would it inflict on his own little family?

When Sarah finally did arrive home in Saratoga Springs there was a letter awaiting her from her father. She had written him that Ellen needed a little change from her life in Saratoga and he had found a house near Louisville that he thought she might like. Mansfield had become increasingly difficult in his behavior and Sarah did not know whether the new baby's coming would change the atmosphere, but from past instances, she held out little hope for it. She felt it might be best if Ellen and Mansfield went to Kentucky after the birth of the baby and had a chance to sort out their affairs, living in a home of their own without their parents underfoot. She felt too that this move would give her father a chance to become reacquainted with her family for he did not have many years left to enjoy his grandchildren.

When Sarah told Reuben of her plan, he could not believe what he was hearing, yet he was not totally surprised by this news. He had realized for some time the instability of Mansfield that could well lead to marital trouble with Ellen. He agreed with Sarah that it might be better if the couple were living under their own roof but did it have to be Kentucky, just at this particular time of trouble in national affairs? He heaved a sigh as he sat down wearily in the big leather chair that was worn by years of use. He was less cheered than ever by this new turn of events that would take his son and beloved daughter-in-law and little grandchildren far away from Saratoga Springs. He would miss those little grandchildren, although their noise and boundless energy had sometimes grated on his senses. He could not escape a presentiment that the troubles within his own family were wearing him out. Mansfield and Ellen needed to work together and try to get along for their family's sake. Somehow Mansfield had never been able to assume responsibility or control his emotions and Reuben could not help the usual parental emotion that perhaps he had been too busy trying to earn a living and establish a place for himself in the world to give the children the guidance they needed as they were growing up. He felt there never was a more conscientious mother than Maria, so the fault could not be hers that Mansfield's nature was so arrogant and irresponsible. However, Reuben realized it was now too late to hope there would be a change in his behavior.

He mused to himself that he was an old man and that he did not like these upsetting changes that were taking place all around him, not only with his own family, but in his country also. His heart bled for both of them and there did not seem to be a thing he could do about either problem anymore.

Chapter Seventeen

Pleasant, warming days of spring merged into the first wave of stifling summer heat and humidity when Mansfield Tracy Walworth Jr. was born at Saratoga Springs on June 19, 1861. Before the day that Ellen gave birth to her second son, the nation had been ripped apart by a crash of gunfire in South Carolina. The fundamental interests of the southern states were irreconcilable with those of the North. The many unsuccessful attempts to come to terms with the North ended on April 12, 1861, with the firing on the Federal Battery at Fort Sumter in Charleston harbor. It seemed as if the world that the Walworths and the Hardins had known before had been totally disrupted by that event.

Tensions were running high within the little family that resided at Pine Grove. War preparations went forward all over the North and, following Lincoln's call for volunteers, lines were forming outside the conscription offices with young men eager to find a place in the front lines to pick off "Johnny Reb." Lemuel kept his own counsel in all of this, trying to weigh the question on all sides, but he could not forget his Southern heritage and he felt his loyalties lay below the Mason-Dixon Line. He was not quite ready to make a decision that would sign him up for a

Ellen Hardin Walworth
Ca, 1900

Courtesy : DAR Museum

Pine Grove
Saratoga Springs, N.Y.

The home of the Walworth family at 525-27 Broadway
Courtesy: Historical Society of Saratoga Springs

Reuben Hyde Walworth
1788-1867

Chancellor, Equity Court of New York State,
1828-1848
Courtesy: Historical Society of Saratoga Springs

Maria Walworth
1795-1847

First wife of Chancellor Walworth
Courtesy: Historical Society of Saratoga Springs

Mansfield Tracy Walworth
1830-1873

Courtesy: Historical Society of Saratoga Springs

Ellen Hardin Walworth
1832-1915

Circa 1865
Courtesy: Historical Society of Saratoga Springs

The children of Mansfield & Ellen Walworth

Front: Francis "Frank" Walworth
Middle: Reubena and Clara Walworth
Rear: (L to R) Ellen, Mansfield "Tracy" Walworth,
unidentified female.
Courtesy: Historical Society of Saratoga Springs

Sarah ~~Susan~~ Smith Walworth
1811-1874

Second wife of Chancellor Walworth
Courtesy: Historical Society of Saratoga Springs

General Martin Hardin
1837-1923

Brother of Ellen Hardin Walworth
Courtesy: Historical Society of Saratoga Springs

**Father Clarence Walworth, 1820-1900
sitting in the library at Pine Grove**

Courtesy: Historical Society of Saratoga Springs

Historical St. Mary's Church, Albany, NY
Organized in 1797

Photo by Thomas De Sorbo

Francis "Frank" Hardin Walworth
1853–1886

Courtesy: Historical Society of Saratoga Springs

The Walworth Mansion at 525-27 Broadway, Saratoga Springs

Courtesy: Historical Society of Saratoga Springs

Camp Wyckoff, Montauk, Long Island

Established for sick and wounded soldiers of the Spanish-American War, 1898.

Theodore Roosevelt Collection Harvard College Library

**The Saratoga Monument, Stillwater, NY
The monument commemorates General
Burgoyne's surrender of the British forces
to General Gates of the American forces
on October 17, 1777**

Courtesy: Saratoga National Historical Park

Reubena Hyde Walworth
1867-1898

Courtesy: Historical Society of Saratoga Springs

Ellen Hardin Walworth
Circa 1890-1892

"An American Patriot"
Courtesy: Historical Society
of Saratoga Springs

position in the army, but he spoke with his mother, telling her he had talked with Ellen and she was agreeable to his going along with her family to Kentucky. He felt he could be of some help to Ellen at this particular time and he also wanted to have more time to think over the matter that weighed most heavily on his mind.

Sarah, in her turn, had been worrying and wondering just what course Lemuel might take and she felt perhaps it would be a good thing for him to have a change of scene, and also, he certainly could be of assistance to Ellen and her family. Unhappy as she was to see both her children leaving her own circle, even though some of it was at her own suggestion, it made her anxious to think that perhaps one brother would end up fighting against the other. She knew in her heart, however, that her own loyalties to her sons would never be divided.

Only awaiting the arrival of their baby kept Ellen and Mansfield from starting on their journey to Kentucky. In the long days of waiting Ellen was kept busy sorting and packing their household belongings in preparation for the move. Cartons were taken to the station and placed aboard a freight train weeks in advance of the move, a trip which was to prove to be a long, slow journey. By the time they were ready to leave at the end of July, only their immediate clothing remained to go with them. Mansfield's disposition was much improved by the prospect of a new location and he seemed more cheerful and helpful. Although he often went out on mysterious errands that meant nothing to anyone but himself, he was so anxious to get started that he even ventured to assist with the packing and crating.

Sarah Hardin Walworth was very fearful of the move at this particular time. She felt that Lemuel had his sympathies with the South and that if he went to Kentucky, in time he would be called to fight. Martin had cast his lot with the Union and was at the forefront of activity in Washington. Ellen, who had grown quite fond of her adopted city and all its historical association with the Revolutionary War, was now moving into Southern territory. She might be forced to take sides, when her loyalties were really in both directions. It was with a sense of foreboding that Sarah and Reuben bid the little family goodbye on the station platform as they began a tedious journey southward.

The ride to New York was as uneventful as it could be with four children between the ages of eight and six weeks. However, when they boarded the train for Washington, they found it already crowded with civilians, mostly men, who, from the cases they carried, looked to be bound for the capital on some kind of government business. It was also jammed with blue-uniformed soldiers, probably heading to join the ranks around the capital. Mansfield searched vainly for a pair of seats. Finally, on their second trip through the coaches, a group of young soldiers got up and offered their seats to Ellen, Mansfield, and the children, while they squatted in the aisle. This was only the start of many unpleasant incidents on the way South. More than once in the short distance between New York and Washington, their train was side-tracked so that a lumbering freight train could pass. Mansfield felt it was probably troops or war supplies headed southward that caused the delays.

When they arrived in Washington, there were no hotel rooms available and the little group sat in the lobby of the Willard while Mansfield and Lemuel scoured the streets for a room in a private home where they might put up for the night. Finally, they were able to return to the fretting children and the weary Ellen and lead them to a place where they could wash up and spend the night. The next day proved little better than the first; it was into the third day before they alighted at the railroad station in Louisville. Although everyone else was exhausted, the rigors of the trip had seemed only to stimulate Mansfield. He cast his eyes keenly over the sight of all the busyness at the station. There were men with only a gun slung over their shoulder, apparently coming to join the army ranks on one side or the other. If all of the boats in the river were any indication, the Ohio and Mississippi rivers were going to be very busy for a long time. Mansfield thought it quite probable that the Union would have many troops around the area before too long, fighting to gain control of the Mississippi.

Lemuel reminded Mansfield that Kentucky was a touchy spot at the moment because just across the river was Union territory and Kentucky was considered as yet a border state. He felt there must be many conflicting emotions in the area, even though Kentucky had a heritage nearer to the South than the North, especially with the use of slave labor. Having lived in Saratoga, he had a respect for the power and drive that the North could exhibit, but he for one did not think the struggle would be over in a short time, or that it would be easy, as did so many others.

Mansfield could not agree with Lemuel and reminded them all that he himself had always admired the elegant Southerners with their gracious manners, their fine racehorses, their splendid mansions and beautiful furnishings and accoutrements, often imported from abroad. He reiterated again that the South had always been known for the amenities of gracious living and the code of the gentleman and he for one would be sorry to see them lose it to crass material interests.

Ellen's grandfather had sent a surrey to pick up the family at the station and the luggage was loaded into a farm wagon. The group headed along the road to their new home, Bird's Nest, a comfortable country place a short distance outside of Louisville. Ellen had a servant girl to help with the children and household duties, as well as a man to work in the yard and tend the horse, cow, and few chickens they needed to provide some of their essential food needs and transportation.

After they were settled in the house, Mansfield often kept himself closeted with his writing or took the horse to ride off to Lexington or Louisville for hours and sometimes a day or two at a time. As the months went by, he was absent for longer and longer periods of time and became abusive when Ellen dared to question him about these wanderings. He reminded her that he had to look into prospects of starting up a law practice so that he would be able to feed his family, and this reassured her for a short time, but still nothing seemed to be forthcoming in that sphere. He was jealous of the fact that the family took up so much of Ellen's time, but he himself did little to help the situation. When she questioned him again about his absences, he remind-ed her that she probably suspected him of going into Louisville to bawdy houses, and for all the love and attention he got at home he might just as well do that. He complained bitterly that no one was interested in him and his feelings and what difference did it make to anyone if he were absent. With that statement, he announced to her that he was going to leave in a few days any-way and would be away for an undetermined period. He said he might even join the army and he had not even yet decided which army it would be.

With these bitter words, he mounted the horse and rode down the road toward Louisville, leaving Ellen to pound her fists into the pillow and weep until it seemed as if there could never be any more tears. Apparently, their argument had awakened Frank, the oldest child, for he timidly knocked on the door of the bedroom and asked if she were all right in a hollow, frightened voice. Ellen called him to come in and drew him tenderly down on the bed beside her. She told him that his father had gone away for a while and that they would all have to be strong and brave while he was gone and keep themselves busy. She praised Frank for being such a good help to her in so many ways, knowing she would be depending on the child-man more and more as the days went by.

Chapter Eighteen

A few weeks after Mansfield's abrupt leave-taking, Ellen received a letter from him. He was in Washington, and his father had secured for him a position as a government clerk. He said he would send her what money he could spare to help with the household expenses. As she read his letter, Ellen could not help but think it looked as if this time the separation of the couple would be a long one. She tried valiantly to overcome the sinking feelings of desolation and isolation that sometimes seemed to overwhelm her. She wrote frequent letters to her mother and Reuben, but not wanting to worry them with her troubles, she tried to conceal them as best she could.

In the long, quiet evenings at the country house, Ellen could look back over her life with Mansfield and realize that the love they had once borne each other had turned into ashes and tears. When Mansfield was home, they rarely spoke to one another; they had lost touch completely with each other's feelings; conversation only seemed to lead to another argument, and when they did speak, their tones of voice were often harsh and bitter. The occasional times when they made love brought only physical satisfaction, but no communion of endearment to one another.

Even though it was an emotional relief that Mansfield was away, Ellen still worried because she did not know where he was or if he would ever come back to her and the children. But it seemed as if he was always drawn back after a time, as when he had been in New York City, and when he did come home he would be his old lovable self with them all for a few days. Even with Lemuel in and out of the house, the days were long and lonely, although the activities of the children kept her busy. Occasionally Ellen took them for a drive to visit acquaintances or her grandfather, but she dreaded their asking about Mansfield and having to give some contrived answer as to why he was not with them at this time.

Struggling through the routine of daily life on a country farm and bringing up four children, often alone, seemed to occupy her every waking minute. Also, social life had all but come to a standstill in Louisville as it had almost everywhere else. All were preoccupied with the war effort, the disappearance of the able-bodied men to the war fronts, and the state of mourning that many were in with the arrival of each new casualty list. Once in a while, a stranger would ride up to the house to ask if Lemuel were at home. Ellen always tried to pretend he had just gone off on business and would be back shortly, fearful of letting them know that she was alone with the children and servants.

Nothing ever seemed to come of these inquiries and after a while she put them to the back of her mind. That Lemuel was off on some mysterious errands was not her business. She welcomed him when he came back periodically, but did not question him concerning his activities. Lemuel knew enough of Mansfield's frequent desertions of his family that he could console her in her troubles and loneliness, but he never ventured any opinion about Mansfield. However, the next time that Lemuel had to leave he did tell her that he had to go off again on business, very serious business and it was better that Ellen not know the nature of it. However, he mentioned it to her so if anything untoward should happen, she would not be surprised.

Ellen had some suspicions, but she thought it was just as well if she did not know what they were, for then she would not be lying if someone came to the house to ask for Lemuel as they sometimes did. She did know these frequent absences were connected with the war in some way and that would not stop her worrying about Lemuel's safety. She always gave a sigh of relief when she saw him come riding down the road toward Bird's Nest after he had been absent for a while.

Before too many months passed, she was to learn that Lemuel's business and absences had much to do with John Hunt Morgan's Confederate guerrillas. This fast-moving cavalry band made a number of raids through Ohio, Kentucky and Indiana, spreading a reign of terror throughout those regions. Quiet, gentle Lemuel was a member of that band.

The reds and yellows of a mild Kentucky fall turned into the bleakness of December. That same bleakness extended to the Christmas that was celebrated at Bird's Nest by Ellen and the children, now bereft of both father and uncle to help in the preparations for the holiday. Ellen could not help but think how Mansfield had changed her from "a dependent wife to an isolated woman alone with little children." Her resentment of his treatment of them festered sorely in her heart, but when a package of toys arrived just before the holiday from Washington, bearing Mansfield's handwriting, she felt a little more kindly toward him. It stirred the hope that perhaps he would return once again to the family fold, as he had done so many times in the past. She had come to Kentucky that summer of 1861 in such high hopes of a new beginning. She had not been living at Bird's Nest for more than six months when that hope was dashed. The thought had never entered her head when Mansfield left her and the children for Washington that she would not see him again for more than three years.

One day she heard a commotion in the front yard and looked out the window to see Lemuel and two other men dismounting and tethering their horses and talking earnestly together. Something in their attitude sent a sense of foreboding through her and she had to swallow a huge lump in her throat before she could go to the door to greet the men.

As they came inside, Lemuel shoved aside her offer of refreshment and suggested they go into the parlor away from the children because he had something important to tell her. Trying not to show the anxiety that seemed to be pushing the very breath out of her chest, Ellen led the way down the hall and the straight backed chair she sat down in seemed necessary to bolster her entire body. The men came directly to their story—they had come to tell her that her husband, Mansfield Walworth, had been arrested in Washington on a charge of spying for the Confederate government.

She could hardly comprehend what they were saying. Mansfield had never in his entire lifetime been able to definitely commit himself to anything for very long. That he should now take such a step seemed to her improbable. She wondered if this could have been the reason for his unexplained absences and just who might have gotten him mixed up in such schemes.

As these thoughts tumbled through her brain, she became full of fears and questions for Mansfield's safety. The men told her he was in jail and it would not be possible for her to go to him at this time, but he could write to Ellen. She was assured that

Chancellor Walworth had been notified of the arrest and he would probably do what he could for Mansfield, although spying was a very serious charge.

Ellen wanted to know every detail of the case and although it was very hard for Lemuel to tell her all, he felt it was only proper that he should. He related that a lady had come to Washington the past fall, claiming to be French, but she was really a Virginian by the name of Mrs. August Morris. She had lived in Paris where she married and had two little boys. When she appeared in Washington, she went directly to the War Department and the State Department and made an offer to reveal Confederate Army signals to the U.S. government for the price of ten thousand dollars. She had no takers for the offer, and the Chief of Staff and the State Department officials had her put under surveillance by Pinkerton men. During the winter she cut a social swath in the city and was very attractive to many men in town. Unfortunately, when the officials went to arrest her in the fashionable Brown's Hotel a few days before, they found Mansfield in the room with her.

Everything in the room swam dizzily before Ellen's eyes as she tried to take in all that Lemuel had told her. No hint in Mansfield's behavior or conversations had prepared her for anything like this revelation. She had never, in all of their disagreements or separations, had any inkling that Mansfield might be involved with another woman. As to the charge of spying, Mansfield had never done anything to seriously indicate he had any great interest in the causes of either the Confederacy or the Union.

In a state of shock Ellen rose and walked to a table across the room, where she hastily scribbled off a message to Saratoga for the men to take to the telegraph office in Louisville. As she stood on the porch watching them leave she took a deep breath of air, lifted her head and would not allow her senses to overcome her. Bringing all her inner strength to the fore, she made a conscious effort to walk slowly across the porch and into the house where the children were eating their lunch in the dining room. While they were napping, she would sit down quietly and sort out the confusing thoughts that were pounding through her temples, and she would seek out the hired man and send him into town to try to purchase any newspaper that might be available.

Chapter Nineteen

Reuben sat in his big leather chair in the library, his long grey hair framing his face and his deep-set, penetrating eyes closed in despair and reverie. A message had come from Washington, telling him of his son's arrest and the charge of spying for the Confederacy. Reuben could not help but wonder whatever had possessed Mansfield to go to such extremes. It had seemed that some of his actions went beyond his uncontrollable temper and almost bordered on the maniacal, but Reuben would never have thought he would get mixed up in such a serious charge as spying. It seemed to Reuben incredible that such an accusation could be made about someone in his own family.

Sarah had come in with her telegram from Ellen in her hand and asked Reuben what should be done and if they should go to Washington at once. She feared for Ellen and the poor little children and wondered whatever should become of them now with their father and husband incarcerated in prison. Reuben assured her that of course they would leave at once, he for Washington and Sarah for Kentucky.

Arriving in Washington, Reuben went immediately to the Old Capitol Prison, where Mansfield was being held. A shudder went through Reuben's mind as the prison cell doors closed behind him. It took all of his determination to walk upright and keep his dignity as waves of anxiety swept over his once power-ful frame, now a bit stooped and shrunken with the weight of seventy-four active years. A much chastened Mansfield greeted his father when they met in the visitor's cubicle. Chancellor Walworth could not keep back his tears when he took Mansfield into his embrace.

Mansfield had to confess to his father that the charges against him were indeed all too true, but that he had never imag-ined in the beginning that he would become so deeply involved as he was at this moment. It had all begun, he said, in a spirit of high adventure. He had thought it might give him a base of expe-rience that he could use in one of his novels. He had made a few attempts at contacting intelligence sources while he was in Louisville. Originally, when he first came to Washington in his clerkship position, he had approached Major General John Fremont to offer his services as a secret agent for the Federal gov-ernment, saying he had two avenues of communication from the South, one of which included his wife. Secretary of State Seward had encouraged him, but William Marcy had blocked the scheme. Mansfield told his father he felt Marcy had an interest in Mrs. Morris himself, but of course he could never prove that.

Since the Union had not been interested in Mansfield's capa-bilities, he had turned to the Confederate network and become embroiled deeper than he had intended. He had always admired the wealthy Southern plantation owners and wanted to help them out in their struggle against those who would take their lifestyle away. The whole experience had proved exhilarating at first, and it had seemed so easy. But as time went on, he found his activities became increasingly more risky and secretive. He had become embroiled to the point where there was no turning back.

Reuben could not but harshly accuse Mansfield of becoming intimately involved with Mrs. Morris, infatuated by her charms and caught in the snare of intrigue that she wove around him. He told Mansfield that for a long time he had felt he had an irresponsible, romantic streak in his nature, but never the like of this. He reminded Mansfield that he should not have been thinking only of himself, but that he had a family to consider and to think of the blemish on his name and theirs when the story came out. However, Reuben realized it was now too late for recriminations and that he must try to see what could be done to get some leniency. He reminded Mansfield that the usual penalty for a convicted spy was death.

With a heavy heart but a determined frame of mind, Reuben tapped every source he knew to try to bring about some clemency for his son. When all the facts were brought out, it was found that Mansfield had only been a very small link in a much larger network and that there was no evidence of conspiracy. He had only been socially involved with Mrs. Morris, as were several other Washington blades. When his cousin, John Barbour, had reported Mansfield to the Secretary of State after Mansfield had invited him to his room one evening and paraded before him in a Confederate uniform, it had forged a link that had needed probing by the Union officials. What little information Mansfield was able to give them led to larger investigations and convictions that involved eighty other Confederate sympathizers.

A few days later, Reuben was able to come again to his son in prison and inform him that because of Mansfield's testimony and because he, Reuben, was a man of prominence on the state and national scene with a reputation of the highest integrity and loyalty to the Union, Mansfield was to be given a chance for a parole. When Mansfield heard this, his animosity toward his father made him stubbornly refuse to sign the parole, so he was kept incarcerated. In disgust, Reuben returned to Saratoga Springs. However, he sent one of his friends to Washington to try to urge Mansfield to sign the parole agreement, or to seek some other means of getting him released from prison. In deep distress, Reuben wrote to Ellen, "Mansfield would have been discharged with the others who were given the parole, but for his own folly. It will be of no use for you to go to Washington, but if you still feel you must do so, I shall be agreeable to paying for your travel expenses." Ellen did not attempt the journey to Washington, and in April of 1862, Mansfield finally agreed to take the parole.

Reuben wrote a long letter to Sarah, who was still in Kentucky with Ellen. In the letter he expressed his deep loneliness without her and closed by saying, "I am broken and desolate over the troubles in my own family and heartsick over the state of the nation."

Meanwhile, Mansfield was sent home to Pine Grove, to wait out the war there, in the custody of his father. Under the conditions of the parole, he was not allowed to leave Saratoga Springs without the written consent of the War Department.

Since he was cloistered in Saratoga, Mansfield had plenty of time to work at his novel writing and in 1863 he published "Lulu," a story of a charming lady living by the banks of the Mohawk River in an old mansion. He incorporated into the tale an Indian legend of mysterious happenings at a lake and its haunted spring (Saratoga Lake and the mineral springs of the area). The theme was cloyingly sentimental with lyrical scenes of nature and of the beauty of the manor property and New York townhouses of the

SARATOGA SOJOURN

wealthy. In the story, a lengthy legal suit between cotton manufac-
turers exemplifies the theory that men of indigence and obscurity
rose to positions of wealth and power.

A young lawyer was the hero of the book, and in a shipwreck
on Long Island, he rescued a beautiful young lady whom he could
not forget, even though he eventually became engaged to his
lovely cousin. Womanhood is portrayed as beautiful, gracious,
charming, and self-sacrificing and women were usually members
of an elegant and wealthy society group. When the cousin finally
eloped with another suitor, Harry Carter, the hero was free to pursue and capture his noble beauty of the shipwreck.

Mansfield wrote about that with which he was familiar and
his story settings were well known to him. His wild and passionate imaginings were well revealed in his literary endeavors.

Chapter Twenty

Only four months after Mansfield's release from prison and his return to parole in Saratoga Springs, a new crisis evolved to disrupt any family calm that might have settled over Pine Grove. It was almost prophetic that Lemuel had arrived from Kentucky to pay a visit to his mother and Reuben. On August 29, 1862, as Reuben glanced from his office window, he caught sight of a boy from the telegraph office coming toward the house. Reuben hastened out of the front door to intercept the boy before anyone else could be alerted. He had a premonition of disaster as he shakily took the envelope in his hand and tore it open. Going back into the house, he uttered a low groan and called in a shaky voice for Sarah to come to his office.

Fearing something amiss from the tone of Reuben's voice, Sarah hurried into the office where her eyes fastened on the yellow sheet in her husband's hand. All at once, she knew the telegram concerned the matter of her son Martin and feeling faint, she had to sit down in the nearest chair, but she still reached out her hand for the message.

As he handed the telegram to her, Reuben steadied his hand and voice and assured Sarah that Martin was not dead, but he was wounded, twice in fact, once at the battle of Groveton and again, more seriously, during the battle of Second Bull run. He felt they should be thankful the wound was only in the shoulder, and that it would keep him out of action for awhile, so they would not have to worry now about something worse happening to him.

Just then Lemuel, having heard Reuben's call to Sarah, came rushing into the office and as soon as he saw the looks on their faces, he knew something had happened to his brother. Reuben explained the situation to Lemuel and that Martin was in a hospital in Washington. Without a doubt, someone would have to go down there to see to his welfare and give him what care they could, since with all of the terrible battles, there must be a shortage of medical supplies and nursing care.

Of course, Sarah in her agitation burst into tears, saying that Martin had been on the front so long she had lived in fear of something terrible happening to him. She now had to release the feelings she had kept under control for so long. Lemuel went to his mother's side to comfort her. After a few moments of letting the news sink into their consciousness, Lemuel spoke his mind about the matter. He told his mother it was too long and hard a trip to Washington at this particular time for her or Reuben to undertake and he should be the one to go down and take care of his brother. He decided he would start immediately and wire back any news to them when he arrived at Martin's bedside. Sarah still felt her place was at Martin's side and that he needed her now as never before. She felt a mother's place was at the side of her stricken children.

Envisioning another long separation from his wife and also seeing the good sense of Lemuel's proposal, Reuben spoke quietly to Sarah, telling her that what Lemuel suggested was a sound idea. He felt a shoulder wound was not desperate and that perhaps he could even bring Martin back home with him in a short time so he could convalesce at home. Then Sarah could nurse and cajole him to her heart's content.

Sarah sat hesitantly turning this throught over in her mind, her motherly instincts trying not to be submerged by the weight of the men's argument. At last she agreed they were probably correct in their thinking and that it had been a struggle getting back from Kentucky in the spring and it certainly would be a worse journey now to head toward Washington. She enjoined Lemuel to write her every day, however, and keep her well posted with details of Martin's health.

When Lemuel arrived in Washington, he found all in confusion in the capital city. The streets were full of people who had come to Washington like Lemuel himself, to search for loved ones. Wagons and drays were rumbling past constantly, bringing in supplies for the wounded and carting off the dead. Wounded men on litters covered the floor of the U.S. Capitol and overflowed into the building of the Patent Office.

When Lemuel arrived at his brother's bedside, he found Martin in better condition than he had hoped for, but Martin's left arm was totally incapacitated from his wound. It was determined, however, that he could travel, so arrangements were made to send him home on a stretcher to Saratoga within a week. Sarah and Reuben were anxiously waiting on the station platform in Saratoga when Lemuel brought Martin home on the third day of September. Sarah was cheered by the prospect of having Martin at home and she bustled about in motherly concern, doing whatever she could to help him improve. Never again, however, would he have full mobility in his arm.

Reuben could not help remarking one day shortly after the soldier had arrived, that Martin had cut quite a swath with the young ladies around Saratoga, and they certainly were enjoying having a wounded veteran in their midst. The house was soon buzzing with female callers, laden down with jellies and cakes to fatten up the pale hero. Martin merely laughed at all this, but in truth he was flattered and amused by all the attention and his recovery continued rapidly.

Because of Martin's injury, Sarah had put off a planned visit to Ellen in Kentucky, but within a few weeks he was so improved that Sarah again considered going to Ellen. She told Martin how lonely Ellen was and what a fearful strain it was to have the total care of small children, not to mention the mental anguish that Mansfield had put her through. Even though Sarah had seen her in the late spring, still she felt it was her duty to go back there and give Ellen what assistance and consolation she could in a precarious situation. Stonewall Jackson had just recaptured Harper's Ferry and was heading into Kentucky and Tennessee, trying to drive the Federals out of those two states. Sarah felt even if there was not an army near Ellen's home, still there were deserters and hangers-on that revolved around any army and that Ellen should not be all alone with no one but children and servants.

Martin could see that Sarah's duty now was for Ellen and he eased her senses by saying he was feeling quite well himself now. He was having such a good time being pampered and flattered by everyone that he was beginning to feel guilty. He felt it was time he got back to his regiment or at least to the command, to see what duty he might be able to do, as he could not stay on sick leave indefinitely.

Bags were packed and Sarah again left Reuben for another extended absence. By October 15, Reuben wrote to Sarah in Kentucky, "Martin left this evening with Lemuel for Washington." Lemuel then returned to Bird's Nest in Kentucky, and Martin went back into active service, but was given light duty of policing and court-martial work until his recovery should be complete. For his gallant service on the battlefields, he was promoted to major and in a short time to colonel, all very gratifying to his mother.

Sarah made a lengthy stay with Ellen, leaving Reuben to feel more and more alone in the old house. There was little communication between him and Mansfield, the latter cloistered with his writings. Sarah left Saratoga again in the early spring for another protracted visit with her daughter, receiving there a letter from Reuben that said, "I am so very lonely here without your companionship. I implore you to come home to me as I am lonely with only Mansfield for company."

In June of 1863, Martin was granted leave and came to Saratoga to visit his mother. He was now returned to active duty and came through the Battle of Gettysburg unscathed. However, his luck ran out in December of 1863. While he was inspecting the guard of the Orange and Alexandria Railroad at Catlett's Station, Virginia, a group of Moseby's raiders penetrated the Union line in a lightning raid. Martin was again wounded in the same arm that had received a bullet at Bull Run. Sarah was again visiting in Kentucky, so when Martin telegraphed his mother the news, she came to him immediately. Within a few days it was determined that there was no recourse but to amputate Martin's left arm at the shoulder. Sarah's grief at this news resulted in agitated letters to Reuben in which she seemed quite beside herself with worry. However, as Martin continued to improve rapidly after the operation, she went from depths of despair over his condition to a feeling of more confidence in a few days. In time, she took him back to Kentucky to stay with Ellen and recuperate from his amputation.

In May of 1864, Martin again had command of a regiment, in spite of the loss of his arm. Surviving yet another slight wound, he visited Sarah in Washington where she was seeing the Lincolns and lobbying for Martin's promotion to Brigadier General. In June, Abraham Lincoln sent in the nomination and on Sarah's birthday, July 4, she wrote to Reuben, acknowledging her role in obtaining a promotion for her son. She said in her letter, "It is a reward to repay him in some measure for his sacrifices in this unhappy war."

Meanwhile, Lemuel had been fighting through these years on a different front and in 1864 was promoted to colonel in Hunt's guerrillas. He too was wounded in action and came back to Bird's Nest with an injured leg. Recuperating there, he was surprised and alarmed by a letter Ellen received from their brother, Martin.

The letter said that Martin was planning a visit to Bird's Nest that fall. Of course, he did not know that Lemuel was there and Ellen's first thought was that if the two soldiers should meet, Martin might be forced to arrest Lemuel as a Confederate soldier. She feared then he could be sent to some Northern prison camp for his activities. She felt Lemuel must leave at once, but how was it possible to secret a Confederate raider through the Union blockade?

Lemuel knew that as a wounded Confederate he was jeopardizing Ellen and her family by staying at her house and he agreed that Martin would have a perfect right to turn him over to authorities. He told Ellen that if he could get through the blockade, there would be a place for him to stay in Canada. Several of his companions in arms had already fled to Montreal and Lemuel could not see that he would be of any use to his commander for some time, if indeed ever again.

Ellen and Lemuel gave much thought to the trip and a scheme was arranged that would disguise Lemuel as a woman and slip him through the blockade, wearing Ellen's clothing. This plan was successfully carried out after much trepidation and in December of 1864, Lemuel was living in Montreal, where he complained that his only recreation was to drive out to Sacred Heart Convent to see Mrs. General Preston's daughter. He asked his mother to send him some law books so he could study while he was convalescing.

Brigadier General Martin Hardin came to Kentucky that fall for a visit with his relatives and there he met and fell instantly in love with Estelle Graham, granddaughter of a pioneer Kentucky doctor. At the same time, he decided to convert to Catholicism. He, who had previously so opposed Ellen's conversion in 1852 when he was a young student, now seemed to feel Catholicism answered a need he felt to get his own spiritual house in order.

Martin and Estelle were married at Pine Grove on November 15, 1864, with Father Clarence Walworth officiating at the ceremony.

Chapter Twenty-One

⚮

While Mansfield was confined by his parole to stay in Saratoga, Ellen continued to live on at Bird's Nest with the children during and after the war. The hurt that Mansfield had dealt her gave her no desire to see him now or to be a consolation to him when he should be repenting for the grossness of his actions. Any feelings she might have had for him at one time were tucked far away in the back of her consciousness because of his lack of consideration for her and the family.

Since the Union army had early occupied the state of Kentucky, it had not been too difficult to receive letters. Mansfield wrote her impassioned letters from his exile in Saratoga Springs and in them he would promise to come back to her as soon as he could, imploring her to forgive him for any misconduct on his part. He also wrote her other, impertinent letters, wondering if she had taken a lover, what she was doing with her time—was she really spending it alone with the children or was she gallivanting about the countryside from one exciting party to another. He would wonder if she had met any men who piqued her fancy. He had a burning inner conviction she was not living alone and tried to bring this subject up again and again in his letters.

Ellen was cheered by some of his letters, and deeply hurt by others. Since there was no truth to his insinuations, she paid little heed to them, except to assure him that he was having flights of fancy. She wrote him very seldom and in her heart was not at all sure that she would welcome him coming back to the family and to her. In other moments, she tried to remember that in her marriage vows she had promised to love and cherish him before God and her fellow man, and her strong sense of duty reasoned that she should want him to come home again. But the thought of his being caught in the arms of another woman rankled her and contributed to her often cold and disinterested feelings.

Frank was now a gangly lad of twelve, but he took a share of the responsibility around the place that surprised and pleased Ellen. He seemed grave for his age, but had all of Mansfield's charm and good looks. He did well at the academy he attended in Louisville and enjoyed his studies, especially reading and English. He was not only a good student, but proved to be adept in all sports. And, like his Kentucky ancestors, he thoroughly enjoyed horsemanship. The war had precluded Ellen's replacing the horse that Mansfield had ridden away on that last day she saw him, with anything but a rather tired old mare whose only duty was pulling the buggy into Louisville on rare occasions. Her grandmother Hardin had left her a small legacy and, after hostilities ceased, she was able to buy a good riding horse for Frank that made it easier for him to get to school. The girls were maturing, and even little Tracy, at four, was running about and helping the yardman pick up fallen pinecones and sweet gum balls that occasionally littered the lawn. While Ellen's inheritance helped to meet her bills, she needed to conserve wisely, for Mansfield could send her very little money, even though he was doing some law work in Saratoga for his father. She often cut and sewed, hemmed up, and made over the children's garments so they would last as long as possible.

Little Tracy did not even remember his father, and Mansfield was only a vague, shadowy figure to Ellen and Clara. Frank, however, had never forgotten those nights of loud arguments and Ellen's reddened, crying eyes. He was old enough to grasp the significance of his father's crime and although he couldn't understand the reasons for it, he knew in his heart that Mansfield had committed a very serious wrong that had torn the family apart. Frank had a curious sense of revulsion for this man whom he barely knew. Even though Mansfield published a new book in 1864, the children were unimpressed by their father's writing abilities because he was so far removed from their own immediate life.

Mansfield's newest novel, "Hotspur, " was full of parallels in his own life and that of his family. The stories tended to be overly sentimental with great detail on clothes, settings, and properties of the characters. His mother was eulogized as a do-gooder, although Mansfield was sarcastic about the Presbyterian Church and considered the Episcopal Church to be superior in that it had more people of cultivated manners within its congregations who had a familiarity with European culture. The heroine was idealized as Ellen and much attention was made of gentle, self-sacrificing women. The plot was one in which girl spurns boy, he goes away, comes back in disguise and all ends well. The suitor had sown his wild oats in college and was a daredevil—Mansfield himself reincarnated. The setting of the novel took place on an old Dutch manor with the locale of Saratoga with its drooping elms and distant hills. While the story had a strong emphasis on prayer and devotions and a strong depiction of religion, still a murder was committed and the story had a gloomy presence.

With the end of the war, Mansfield's parole was forfeited, and he was again free to come and go as he pleased. Immediately a longing suffused him to see his children. In the boring three-year exile in Saratoga Springs, he had mused on what they must look like and what sort of greeting he would receive from them when he might see them.

Ellen's face had often flashed through his dreaming. Time had begun to erase the memories of domestic squabbles and hurt feelings that had plagued their marriage for years.. He thought only of the warm, rosy glow he would feel on holding her in his arms again in a loving embrace, and his blood coursed hot as he thought of taking her physically once more. He wrote her a long letter of repentance and remorse and voiced his intentions of reconciliation as soon as possible. She in turn, sent him an answer of encouragement, saying that they should try again to revive their faltering marriage and attempt one more time to reconcile, if only for the children's sake.

In the three years she had spent in Kentucky, Ellen had felt a longing to see the city of Saratoga Springs again and to have the children visit their grandfather, Reuben, since he had seen very little of them in the past few years. She knew too that he was becoming more enfeebled and reclusive with each passing year. After a sleepless night of tossing and turning in her bed, she arose with a new conviction and went down the stairs to breakfast. She announced to the children that they would need to get their traveling clothes together as they would be going to Saratoga for a visit that summer and would be making quite a lengthy stay. She reminded them their father was anxious to see them all again and their grandfather had also been pining to see everyone.

Chapter Twenty-Two

❦

The long train journey from Kentucky had seemed tedious to the weary wife and mother and the four young children. However, as the train pulled into the station at Albany, Ellen waved out the window at Mansfield when she saw his lean and handsome figure standing on the platform, and she could not help but think that he was as dashing and handsome as ever. As they came off the train, he ran quickly up to Ellen and thrust a bundle of flowers into her hands. He put his arm around her waist and kissed her longingly. A little shock tingled up her spine at the kiss, and she realized she had missed the presence of a loving man in her life. When he finally disengaged her she laughed that he was just as impetuous as ever and urged him to come and get reacquainted with his little family.

A new toy presented to Tracy soon had him entranced with the handsome stranger that was his father, but the girls were at an age where they could be shy. They politely thanked him for their gift of new dolls and retired to a corner of the station to play with them. Now it was time to turn attention to Frank, standing sullenly aside while watching all this scene of indulgent love.

Ellen coaxed Frank to come forward and shake hands with

his father, reminding him that he was the only one who would remember Mansfield from before the war. Frank advanced to extend his hand stiffly and utter a greeting, then turned on his heel and walked out the station door. Mansfield thrust back into his pocket the shining watch he had been about to proffer to Frank and wondered what he had ever done to receive such a curt welcome from his older son. He presumed the boy was at an awkward age and that this homecoming was an embarrassment to him. He felt sure Frank would come around once he had been in Saratoga Springs for a time and gotten used to the fact that Mansfield was his father and had a rightful place in the family.

Ellen took Mansfield's arm as they walked away and assured him Frank was like him in many ways. Frank had a flair for writing poetry and was a good student with organizational talent that might presume his studying to be a lawyer. She also reminded Mansfield that Frank was going to be just as handsome as his father with maturity and that he was very accomplished in riding and shooting. She reminded Mansfield what a help and comfort Frank had been to her in the past three years and that mother and son were very close to one another.

Life went along smoothly for the first few weeks of Ellen's visit to Saratoga Springs, and she began to think that perhaps they could rebuild their life as it had been in the first years of their marriage. She did notice that Mansfield wanted to know her every movement, and if she went downtown at all, he was full of questions about where she went while there and what she did.

One day, Reuben told Ellen there were some dear old friends staying at the United States Hotel in Saratoga and, having arrived the day before, they wanted Sarah and Reuben to pay them a call at once. When Sarah sent a message of acceptance, the friends insisted that Mansfield's family come along also. On hearing this, Mansfield quickly and sharply asked to be counted out on the visit, saying he would stay at home and attend to his writing. He could not imagine Ellen would want to go either, since they had had such a short time together again.

Ellen tried to persuade him to go, reminding him of the old friendship with the visitors and that Reuben's feelings should be considered in the matter. With that, Mansfield ranted on that no one seemed to consider his feelings and angrily slammed out of the parlor and out the front door into the street.

That evening, the little group went off on their visit to the former acquaintances, returning shortly before nine. Ellen sent the children off to their rooms and went to her bedroom door. Finding it locked, she called to Mansfield as she again tried the unyielding knob, holding little Tracy by the hand. She said she had to come in to put Tracy to bed and asked that the door be opened.

Suddenly the door flew open to reveal a disheveled Mansfield. He grabbed Ellen's arm with a quick movement and pulled her roughly into the bedroom with Tracy stumbling along behind. He ranted that she was up to her old tricks again, having a good time while he sat at home alone. He accused her of knowing he wanted her with him that evening but she deliberately went off anyway. Completely ignoring the little boy who stood bewildered at all the commotion, he began ripping at the buttons on the bodice of her dress as she beat at him fiercely with her fists. She warned him that he would have the household aroused and that he was frightening little Tracy. As she started toward the whimpering child, Mansfield commanded her to stop and send Tracy out into the hall. In a new tirade, he told Ellen she could no longer hide behind that loving mother facade and now that this was started he was going to finish it. He gave Tracy a shove into the hall and told him to go to Frank's room for the night. Turning to Ellen, he told her he was tired to death of her putting him off all the time, that he needed her tonight and he was going to have her, even if against her will.

He grabbed her to himself again and proceeded to alternately shake her and rip off her clothing. She beat back, but his strength was too much for her. He flung her onto the bed as his hands probed and ripped at her garments, and his hot hands fondled her as he made his advantage. In a blinding rage at his brutish will, she felt the hot warmth of his passion flood through her as she tried vainly to fight against his superior strength.

The next morning, a pale and worn looking Ellen came downstairs to announce that she and her children would be leaving Saratoga within the week. The children realized that something dreadful had happened between their parents the night before that had prompted this sudden departure. Ellen asked her mother to accompany her back to Bird's Nest and Sarah spent considerable time there throughout the year of 1865.

Mansfield, in his turn, came down the stairs with valise packed, ready to take the next train to New York City. He left his children quickly, not even turning to answer their farewell waves as he hastened down the path and out the gate. In New York, he continued to work at his writing, but he had very little money to send his family. Ellen's debts were mounting as she tried to support her little group. In frequent letters to Reuben at Saratoga, Sarah asked him for loans for Ellen to help pay the bills. Ever playing the mother role, Sarah felt her first duty was to her children even though that duty might require long absences from her husband's home.

In January of 1866, Lemuel Hardin married Ann Jacob of Lynnford, Kentucky. He was studying law at Caldwell Brothers in Louisville and stayed with that firm until 1879. Having two children in Kentucky was another reason for Sarah to relinquish time with Reuben in Saratoga Springs.

Apparently, Mansfield had time in New York to reconsider his behavior, and feeling much chagrined, asked permission to visit his family in Kentucky in the fall of 1865. In November, Ellen took seven-year-old Clara with her on a visit to Pine Grove and New York City. Early in 1866, however, Ellen was back in Kentucky alone. By May, she had received a letter from Mansfield, asking for another try at a reconciliation and suggesting he would be willing to come to Kentucky, for a time at least. Ellen held on to the hope that they would again establish a normal family life at Bird's Nest and welcomed Mansfield when he appeared in Louisville. For a few months the reconciliation seemed to go along smoothly. Before long Ellen had happy news to communicate to Mansfield—she was again expecting a child, due in early 1867.

Mansfield was ecstatic but realized that if she was pregnant, it would change their plans for traveling to Saratoga to visit their parents. He felt that taking all of the children and traveling in warm weather would be too exhausting for Ellen and he suggested that perhaps he should go alone with their son, Frank. Ellen felt that because of the Chancellor's impaired health and because of his age and suffering with diabetes, it was imperative that Mansfield go and she was pleased he wanted to include Frank in the travel.

That visit by Mansfield and Frank to Saratoga encouraged the Chancellor to give his precious library to his grandson Frank, in the hope it would encourage the lad to become a distinguished lawyer and make his mark in the world. Sarah was pleased and relieved he had given the books to Frank for she said the

Chancellor harbored a dreadful fear that after he was gone the library would be divided and go to strangers. Now he could take comfort in the fact that his own grandson would have it in safe-keeping.

The new baby was born in February 1867 and named Reubena Hyde Walworth in honor of her illustrious grandfather. By July 1867, Sarah was again in Kentucky and complained in letters to Reuben about Ellen's lack of funds. Mansfield visited Kentucky that summer, but he had gone again to live in New York, where he said he could better attend to his writing. In 1867, his novel, "Stormcliff," was published but that did not fatten his pocketbook to any considerable extent.

This novel was another tale of the highlands of the Hudson featuring a handsome, masterly hero who was a writer (Mansfield?). There were tales of witchcraft by an old woman named Nora, and the extensive property and wealth of the father was devised to another. The power and majesty of God was also a central theme and he extolled the Christian virtues of the hero-ine, Grace Baltimore. Mansfield based some of his fictional char-acters on his mother, a role of loving reformer, working with poor outcasts. In his story, a small, white, satin-like rose that grew in the garden was named "Lady Walworth."

Chapter Twenty-Three

Little Reubena was never to know the great personage whose name she bore, as her first journey nine months later was to Saratoga Springs for Reuben Walworth's funeral. The tragedies and estrangements within his own family and his exertions to keep the Union together in the last final days before the declaration of war and the dreadful conflict itself proved to be the straw that broke the iron will of the Chancellor. The fact that he was a great man who was widely loved and respected in many circles was repeated in obituaries and eulogies. His capabilities and devotion to his ideals and to his country had never been in question. But a decline had set in that overshadowed the last years of his life, and he had become a recluse within his beloved Pine Grove. He had grown increasingly lonely and despondent over the frequent absences of Sarah. In the fall of 1867, an old associate visited Reuben and he remarked on the air of melancholy about the place—even the very trees looked sad and drooping. "We found him no longer master of that house; he was instead a guest where he had been the proud head of the house." Reuben died on Thanksgiving Day and was laid out among his books in the library at Pine Grove.

His friends and former associates heaped lavish praise upon his many and varied accomplishments, and recalled his love of social life. They remembered that he often invited lawyers and petitioners to dine with him after adjourning court; he enjoyed going to and giving parties. To the last year of his life, he always paid New Year's calls on his many acquaintances. His abstinence from liquor was a lifelong covenant. He had organized the New York State Temperance Society in 1829 and was its first president. Though his view of justice was austere and uncompromising, his knowledge led him to the presidency of Albany Law School in 1853 and honorary degrees from Harvard and Yale. Ellen remembered him becoming as a child himself when he played croquet with his grandchildren and felt him "a kind friend in spite of his peculiarities."

Even in death, Reuben and Mansfield were at odds with one another. Reuben's will left the bulk of his estate in trust for his widow, and a few bequests to his children and others. His son-in-law, Reverend Jonathan Backus and son Clarence were to be the executors. His will stripped Mansfield of all control of a small inheritance by appointing Clarence as administrator of the funds. He did leave Mansfield a Walworth family seal and a decorative portfolio that had belonged to Maria. The terms of the will clearly showed to the world that the father felt a strong distrust of his erratic and rebellious younger son. Clarence was left in a compromising position. To his credit, he refused the trusteeship and had the U.S. Trust Company appointed in his stead.

The will also directed Clarence to write or to pay someone to write the Chancellor's biography. If Mansfield was chosen to write it, he would receive the profits from its sale. Leaving for New York immediately after the reading of the will, Mansfield wrote to Ellen, "The only reason he did not omit my name from his will altogether was that he hoped I would write his life. He knew nobody else would." The rift that had existed for so long between Mansfield and his father only compounded in the Chancellor's death. Mansfield raged against his father and his brother Clarence, for weeks afterward.

Meanwhile, Ellen decided it was time to take a new course of action now that Frank was ready for college. She sat down to write her brother Lemuel a lengthy letter. "I feel our little family had better leave Kentucky for good now and go on to something else, since Frank must go to college and we have so little money to give him for an education. I have already applied for a government clerkship in Washington and am confident of receiving confirmation with no problems, so we will be coming back to Bird's Nest very soon and collecting our belongings.

If we go to live in Washington, as I plan to do, Frank can live at home and attend Georgetown University, so that will ease the financial burden and, of course, so will the wages from my working position. You and Ann need more room for your family. Since I know how much you like the farm, I am perfectly willing to sell you my interest in Bird's Nest. If that will make the financial picture for you a little tight just now, I am sure that Martin can lend you some money. He has no interest himself in the property as you know, since he has left the army and gone to live in Chicago and open a law practice of his own there. I am leaving soon for Washington and will find an apartment for us, and then we will come to Kentucky and pack our belongings. The children can start the new school term in Washington, and I can begin to earn some money that we sorely need."

After this move of his family, Mansfield shuttled between Washington and New York and applied himself to his writing, publishing "Warwick" in 1869. This proved to be the most successful of his works. The family situations in which Mansfield was so intimately involved entered again into this work with his dreamy characterization of Ellen as the carefully educated heroine of great personal beauty, reared in an affluent society; a clerical figure based on the personality of his brother Clarence; an angelic mother safely in heaven, a gentlemanly hero who was a writer (Mansfield again?) that had been disowned by his father, and a brother who was enriched by an inheritance. The novel delved deep into the ways and meaning of Christianity with morality and religion the overpowering themes, and it also attacked the matrimonial theories of the day. As in most of his other novels, a saga of a horse and persons who were superb riders held a place in the tale. The story ends on a note of witchcraft and the sages of ancient history were extolled in great detail.

Mansfield took glory in spending the royalties from his success and living the life of a prestigious writer. In the summer in Saratoga, he was known on the streets for his modish-looking clothes and flamboyant air. Ellen stayed on in Washington for eighteen months, then lost her job when there was a change in administration. This required that the family move back to New York with Mansfield. By this time, Ellen was seriously beginning to doubt Mansfield's sanity, especially when he became so incensed, that at times he kicked and broke the furniture in their apartment. The old harmony was lost once again in bickering and jealous rages, with Mansfield accusing Ellen of seeing other men and wondering if Reubena or the new baby that was on the way was really his own child.

Ellen's only answer to these accusations was to declare that Mansfield must be mad to say such things and that he had no reason to think of her as a frivolous woman for she had never, ever, given him any reason to think and say such dreadful things.

She reminded him she had been loyal to their marriage vows in spite of all that had happened over the years, even though she sometimes had grave doubts that he had been loyal.

Mansfield was incensed that she intimated he might be mad and grabbed her arms and cuffed her across the head and beat her upon the arms and shoulders. He flung her across the bed and stamped out of the house in a rage.

This was the second beating she had received from Mansfield during the four months of her latest pregnancy. It was to prove to be the proverbial straw that broke the camel's back. After the first physical abuse, she had shown her bruised arm to seventeen-year-old Frank and, as she recalled in later years, "He had such a look of extreme suffering, which I had never seen before. His reply was, This must not be. I was so alarmed at his reaction that I never told him again of anything of this kind."

After Mansfield left the house, Ellen rose from the bed with a feeling of outrage coursing through her entire body. Her mind, which had hoped and compromised for so many long years, was now fixed firmly on the final objective of this night of January 26, 1871. She quickly washed her face, arranged her hair and clothing, and left the house. She hailed a passing hack to take her to her brother Martin's hotel, where he was staying while on business in New York City.

When she came into his room, she spoke calmly to Martin, telling him that she had come to him for help. She was leaving Mansfield once and for all, and there would be no turning back this time. She reminded Martin how Mansfield had deserted his family time and time again and had been abusive to her. Her children were being constantly upset by all the scenes and absences, and Frank was in inner turmoil over his father's actions and the heartaches that she had to suffer. She asked Martin to prepare the papers for her, as she was filing for divorce at once.

Martin assured her he would stay up all night if necessary to do the legal work and would file the necessary papers the very next morning. He gave her some money to buy a railroad ticket to Saratoga Springs and told her he would come for her and the children early in the morning to take them to the train. He did not want Ellen at the apartment if Mansfield should come back in a day or two.

Martin sent their mother a telegram to alert her of the impending visit, saying that Ellen would stop off for a few hours in Albany to see Father Clarence before journeying on to Saratoga. Ellen felt the need to seek counsel and consolation from Clarence in her dilemma with the divorce proceedings. It was providential that she did not envision what suffering and heartache was yet to come as she shed her marriage ties to Mansfield Walworth.

When Mansfield returned to the apartment in a more contrite mood the next evening, he found Ellen and the children gone and the apartment bare of their belongings. In a rage, he took a pistol from his dresser drawer and rushed to Martin's hotel room. As he dashed across the streets of New York, he fumed that Martin was a scoundrel who had helped them leave the city and had tried to take his wife and little children away from him. Thoughts of killing Martin rocked through his brain. Completely demented, he arrived at the hotel and went directly to Martin's room and imperiously knocked on the door. Martin opened the door and Mansfield pushed his way into the room, screaming invectives at Martin and demanding to know what he had done with his wife and family.

Martin tried to talk reasonably with the agitated man, admitting he had helped Ellen and the children leave the city for they were not safe living in the same house with a madman.

Hearing this, Mansfield drew his pistol, grabbing Martin by the collar and sticking the pistol to his neck. But Martin used his one remaining good arm and struck Mansfield in the face, causing him to drop the pistol. Martin stepped over him and went out the door, running down the hall and calling loudly for help. At the lobby stairs, a policeman and a porter seized the crazed Mansfield as he chased after Martin, screaming that he would kill him if he did not tell him where his wife and family had gone.

Chapter Twenty-Four

⚬⟋⟍⚬

Meanwhile, upon Ellen's return home she had gone first to the rectory of Saint Mary's Church in Albany where Clarence was serving as pastor. Clarence met the family group at the door with tears in his eyes and loving embraces for his little nieces and nephews. After they shared some refreshments, he took Ellen aside and told her there was no way in which he could condone a divorce but that certainly in his own mind he had no doubt but that she surely had been given every provocation for such action by Mansfield. He did tell her she must abide by her own conscience and that he would pray for all of them each day of his life. He advised her to go up to her mother for succor and that they could be a comfort to one another, for surely Sarah was lonely in the house in Saratoga all by herself.

Ellen and her brood returned to her mother's home at Pine Grove. She delivered her baby in June 1871. She knew a sense of guilt in the near relief she felt when the child, Sarah Margaret, lived only a few months. With its father in the condition that he was, she felt it was a blessing that the little girl would never have to go through life as the product of a broken home. She knew too that this would be her eighth and last child, and now her life must take on yet another direction.

The group had only been settled in Pine Grove for a short time when Ellen approached her mother with a plan that had been brewing in her thoughts for some time. She needed money to support her family and she hoped her mother would agree to her opening a boarding school at the house in the fall. She felt she had had plenty of experience in teaching her own children and so she ought to be able to teach others.

Sarah was not unreceptive to the idea, she felt it was necessary for financial reasons, and it would also put some life back into the house to have young people around again. She was herself beginning to feel old and downhearted and knew her grand days of traveling to Washington and Kentucky were coming to an end. She did remark that she guessed Mary Todd Lincoln was in a worse condition than she was with troubles besetting her on every side since they had both lost their husbands.

The move back to Pine Grove proved to be a good one for Ellen and the children. Her mother enjoyed their company and Father Clarence came up occasionally from his parish in Albany, but he was very busy with his church duties and had little time for extended visits. Both of Sarah's sons lived far away, and the Chancellor's daughters, although one lived in Saratoga and two resided in a neighboring city, no longer visited now that he was gone. They had never been close to Sarah, being married and well along with their own family pursuits at the time of their father's second marriage.

Mansfield had been at first shocked and disbelieving and then violently angry at the divorce proceedings, but there was nothing he could do to block the matter. He stayed on in New York City and petulantly declared to anyone who would listen that he hated Ellen and all she stood for, and alternately lamented or was secretly glad she had the children living with her, so he was not distracted by their activities. In his rage over the state of his affairs, he turned to his writing career with a renewed vigor. That was the year in which he finished his latest novel, "Delaplaine," published in 1871. This novel was pure exotica, set with a war theme of Persians and Russians and Armenian monks in which a volcano erupts and the hero of the Russian wars marries a princess.

When Mansfield would stop long enough to contemplate the turn of events his marriage had taken, he would sit down and write abusive, sometimes threatening letters to Ellen. When news reached him that she had opened a boarding school for boys in the family homestead, he became quite livid with rage. Feeling that she somehow demeaned their home by conducting a school there, he repeatedly threatened to come up to Saratoga and tear the schoolroom apart and physically abuse her for entering into such a vocation.

His letters raged on that she was demeaning all of them by working for a living and that she did not need to work to buy her daily bread. He reminded her that he was a successful author and a scion of one of the first families of Saratoga, of a social class that never had its women working for they all had husbands who took care of all their financial needs. He felt it all was a disgrace to the family and he would not tolerate such behavior from anyone bearing the name Walworth. He warned her that if she continued in this wild scheme, he would come up and break her arms so she could never teach or write again. He even told her she should be very careful for if he had a gun in his hand he might shoot her and that all the intensity of hate in his life was centered on her and she should listen for the crack of the pistol.

Frank was of an age that he could sense how upset his mother became whenever she received one of these threatening letters.

Ellen would try to tell him that his father was unpredictable at best and the blustering threats were just a way to work off his anger. She felt she had taken the wisest course in having the marriage dissolved, and that everyone, except perhaps Mansfield himself, was happier and more at peace for it.

Their life at Saratoga was tranquil enough now. Ellen's school was going well and producing the sorely needed income. Frank was attending college at Georgetown in Washington and his sisters, Nelly and Clara, were enrolled at the convent school of the Sacred Heart at Kenwood, a suburb of Albany. This institution was situated on a wooded eminence at the southern entrance to the city and commanded a sweeping view of the Hudson River valley. The school had evolved from an imposing mansion that had been built in 1849 on a large acreage and served as the residence for Mr. Joel Rathbone, a wealthy entrepreneur and builder of cast iron stoves in the city. By 1858, the property had been sold to the Catholic Diocese to serve as the home of the Convent and Academy of the Sacred Heart. The Rathbone mansion was incorporated into new buildings that were erected to house the novitiate. While application to studies was considered very important at the school, the young boarding ladies were also brought up in the attitudes of a select finishing school. Manners and social graces played a prominent place in their education.

Nelly and Clara thus saw much more of Father Clarence than did the rest of the family, since he was so near them, living in the rectory of Saint Mary's on Chapel Street in Albany. He often had the two girls to dinner on a Sunday afternoon, or took them to concerts, lectures, and other social events in the capital city. He was proud to squire about the two vivacious and pretty young girls and to introduce them as members of his family. The girls, for their part, were much taken with this dear, kindly uncle, and he undoubtedly had great influence on their later lives and careers. Perhaps he represented to them a stable father figure, such as had been lacking in their own father. His interest in the girls was innocent enough in some aspects, but it undoubtedly gave Clarence a great deal of personal satisfaction to have their love and respect, and compensated for the children he could never have.

Chapter Twenty-Five

✍

Clarence Walworth was a conscientious and perfect clergy-man. When he had decided in his younger years that he must change his theological beliefs and become a Catholic he never wavered but went on to become a zealous missionary of the Paulist Order in the United States. When his health failed and he had to change the direction of his energies, he resigned from the Paulists and was appointed rector of Saint Peter's Church in Troy, New York. He disliked the trustee system which held the management of that church and felt humiliated in administering under its direction. He went back to the Paulists for a time but that group was laboring under a decision as to whether to remain as it was, to be a congregation without vows, or to be a religious society with vows. When the vote went to the first option, Clarence decided he would resign from the order as he would rather live as a secular priest in his own diocese with his bishop as superior. He wanted to come back to Albany and was assigned to the Cathedral of the Immaculate Conception in Albany for a year, after which he was sent as pastor to Saint Mary's Church in 1866.

Saint Mary's was too small and too old for safety and after

observing conditions there Clarence set about at once to begin construction of a new church. In May 1867, the work was begun on a church building of Romanesque design in brick and stone. The Very Reverend Edgar P. Wadhams, a childhood acquaintance of Clarence's who had gone through early days of conversion with him, laid the cornerstone. Wadhams had been ordained at Saint Mary's in 1850 and appointed an assistant pastor there for a time.

Clarence held the pastorate of Saint Mary's until his death in 1900, and this was to be the most fruitful time of his life. He was a forceful, active priest and a concerned citizen of the city. He put in long hours of work and was a gifted preacher, as well as a dramatic actor. He also had a talent with his pen, writing poems, the "Life of Father Wadhams," and contributing many articles over the years to various newspapers and The Catholic World. In keeping with his interest in history, he held a Military Mass in 1886 to commemorate the 200th anniversary of Albany receiving its city charter. There was present at the mass a delegation of Caughnawaga Indians in tribal costume, as well as city and state officials. These Indians were descendants of the original Mohawks who once roamed over hunting grounds in the vicinity of Albany long before the city's actual existence.

Clarence was so impressed by the acuteness of his nieces that he considered making an expansive offer to Nelly, whom he felt had the greatest inclination to participate in an adventure with him. Accordingly, one day in 1872, he arrived at Pine Grove to put forth his plans to Ellen and to secure her approval of the project before proceeding further with his invitation to the fourteen-year-old girl.

He told Ellen he proposed to take a trip to Europe and perhaps around the world, and he would like Nelly to accompany him as his guest. He thought Nelly had the intellectual capacity and the physical stamina for it, as well as the ability to be an entertaining and enthusiastic companion. He said it would give him great pleasure to show her the wonders of other cultures and that her enthusiasm would be a tonic for him. Ellen was taken aback at this generous offer, but she at once saw the advantages for Nelly in such an undertaking. It was agreed that Nelly herself should be consulted now that Ellen and Clarence were in agreement.

The wheels were set in motion and the next day Nelly was called into the office at the school and told that a note had come from her mother that Nelly should take the train to Saratoga that day, and that it was not bad news but her Uncle Clarence was going away on a trip and she was requested to come up and say goodbye to him. When she reached her home her brother, Tracy, and little sister, Reubena, stood at the front gate, with knowing smiles on their faces.

As soon as she went into the house and greeted the remainder of the family, her mother led the group into the parlor and suggested that everyone be seated so the reason for this sudden call home could be explained to Nelly. She told Nelly that Clarence had a year's leave of absence from his parish and desired to go abroad for a period of rest and recreation and that he had proposed that Nelly accompany him. Ellen reminded the awestruck Nelly that this would mean she would be going away from home and school for almost a whole year, and that she would have to make up her studies when she got back.

Nelly's unbelieving face was wreathed in smiles as she answered that she did not have to think about it at all, she was ready to go at once and could not imagine anything more exciting. A year of travel would be no longer than a year at boarding school and probably much more interesting.

The excitement mounted as preparations for the voyage went forward and the weeks were spent in getting clothing in order and supplies packed. The family accompanied the travelers to New York to see them off on the ship that was bound for Scotland, the first leg of their long journey. The excitement of the jostling crowds at the pier, the actual boarding of the vessel and finding one's stateroom, and the anticipation of what lay ahead removed all thoughts of doubt or homesickness from Nelly's mind. However, when she stood at the rail as the ship slowly receded from the shoreline, she kept her eyes riveted on one waving white handkerchief that was lower than all the rest. Her little brother, Tracy, had been waving it vigorously ever since the boat started away from the pier.

While the preparations for the voyage were being made, Ellen had suggested to Nelly that she write to her once a week, giving the details of her journey. She reminded her the correspondence could serve not only to keep them apprised of her destinations, but it would also serve as a journal of her travels that she would be able to keep as a permanent momento. Nelly felt it a fine suggestion and agreeably complied. At one of her ports of call a few months later she met, by chance, an acquaintance from Albany. "Oh," said the friend, "I am not at all surprised to find you in this far corner of the earth. I have been reading about your travels in The Albany Sunday Press." It came as a pleasant surprise to Nelly to learn her articles were being printed in that paper. Later, at the urging of her Uncle Clarence and other family members, these same articles were published in narrative form under the title "An Old World As Seen Through Young Eyes." Upon returning from her trip, Nelly continued her studies at Kenwood and later became a teacher, first at her mother's school in Saratoga and later at Albany.

Meanwhile, Mansfield Tracy was at school in Saratoga and little five-year-old Reubena was the pride and joy of her grandmother, Sarah. The child had a blond beauty and sweetness of manner that had already made her the pet of the family, but this attention did not seem to make her ever willful or selfish in any way. This sweet and caring nature would prove itself again many times in her later life.

Chapter Twenty-Six

The year was 1872 and Frank was at home in Saratoga Springs when the postman delivered another letter to Ellen from Mansfield. When Ellen opened the letter a grim look came over her face as she saw the familiar handwriting. She tried to manage a smile as she sat down to read it but after a few minutes she quietly put the letter aside, a hurt look suffusing her face. Frank was quick to see the look and knew that his father had said the same nasty comments as usual—that Ellen was a whore and a deceitful liar, that she did not have any compassion because she did not try to understand him and his needs and that he would kill her if she didn't come back to him.

Ellen answered Frank's questioning look by saying that they could not hold Mansfield accountable for his words or his actions. She really thought he was deranged, at least when it came to his feelings about her but that there was not a great deal she could do about that.

Frank thought it must be against the law to write such threatening letters and put them through the mails. He could recall vividly all the bad scenes that happened between his parents when he was a little boy and he remembered how greatly it had distressed Ellen. He believed Mansfield was jealous because Ellen had the love and respect of the family and friends while his father was nothing but a selfish cad and a failure in his relationships. When he thought of all the past torments that Mansfield had caused his mother and the family, Frank could only be filled with a feeling of hatred and loathing toward his father.

Ellen, for her part, did not really believe Mansfield was capable of actually carrying out the threats he wrote in his letters but it broke her heart to realize how much they both failed each other in love and understanding. As the months wore on, more violent letters came from Mansfield, filled with veiled threats that underscored his sense of drama. Ellen was more deeply wounded by each letter. Although she tried to reason with herself that the writer was unbalanced and she should pay little attention to the matter, still she could not hide the heaviness of her spirit.

After August 1872, Frank began a watchful campaign, often intercepting the letters Mansfield sent to Ellen. They became more violent when Mansfield learned she was receiving one third of the trust fund the Chancellor had left for him. He was afraid she would seek more and he accused her of "being a robber of all I possess. You have robbed me of home and children and usurped my place with my own father." His last denunciation of Ellen took place in a letter of May 30, 1873 in which he ranted: "I am going to call upon my children. Their little faces haunt me, as they are my children as well as yours. But, if I do come to call upon them, keep Frank Walworth out of my way. You have taught him to hate me. I shall shoot you and myself upon those doorsteps . . . I say to myself, 'She is teaching them all to hate a broken-hearted father.'"

Ellen went downstairs on the morning of June 2 and noticed Frank's absence from the breakfast table. All the while she was eating a little nagging doubt stuck in the back of Ellen's mind. She did not want to alarm her mother, but as soon as the meal was finished and her mother was installed in the parlor with the morning paper, she went upstairs to Frank's room. On his bedside table was a note that stated he had gone out and would be gone all day. Everything in the room seemed to be in order, but her curiosity urged her to look into the closet and she noticed one of his suits was missing so he had probably worn that. As she searched among the papers on his desk, she found an envelope in Mansfield's handwriting.

Immediately, she wondered if Frank had gone off to New York to see Mansfield. She knew he had been very upset about all of her problems with his father but she knew Frank well enough to know he would not just go off on any kind of trip and never even mention it. There must be some very urgent reason if he had gone off in such haste.

Suddenly a frightful thought entered her mind and she hoped if they did meet one another they would both keep their heads. She knew if Frank tried to argue with Mansfield, it would only end in a clash of wills with a very doubtful outcome. She was now sure he had gone to see his father because of that envelope and that he had kept the letter it contained away from her to spare her feelings. She knew she must contact a friend in New York right away and see if he could locate Frank.

Frank had quietly left the house on North Broadway in the early hours of the morning and walked away quickly to board the train for Albany; once there, he purchased a one-way ticket to New York City. He was so preoccupied that he barely remembered the train trip. Once in New York he made a purchase at a pawn shop and went to the Sturdevant House Hotel, where he registered at 3 P.M. He then went to his father's boarding house and, since

Mansfield was not in, left a note for his father. On the morning of June 3, Mansfield appeared at Frank's door at 6:15 A.M.

A shouting match ensued in which Frank accused his father of trying to humiliate his mother and frightening her with threats of her life. Mansfield, in his turn, screamed that Ellen had turned his babies against him and shut him out of his own house with the divorce proceedings. He screamed that he could not hold up his head in public anymore for the shame of that scandal and that he hated even the mention of her name and he hated Frank too for taking her side in the matter.

With this utterance, Mansfield reached toward his coat pocket and Frank, fearing that he was going for a pistol, pulled out his own and, in his rage and despair, fired four shots at his father. Mansfield fell to the floor, clutching his chest as a dark stain appeared on the front of his fine linen shirt. Frank's aim had proved fatal.

Stepping over his dying father and walking calmly down the stairs, Frank went to the hotel desk and paid his bill, sent a telegram to his uncles Martin and Clarence, and walked to the nearest police station. Going up to the desk, he quietly stated to the policeman on duty, "I have just shot and killed my father."

Ellen and Clarence arrived at the Tombs Prison on June 4 to see Frank, but returned to Saratoga on Thursday, June 5 for Mansfield's funeral. Ellen told Clarence that in one of Mansfield's fits of temperament, he had accused her of influencing his decision to become a Catholic and he had emphatically renounced his Catholic faith. Now they were left with a decision to make as to who would officiate at the funeral service. Ellen felt they must have the pastor of the Presbyterian Church in Saratoga Springs perform the rites because of the long involvement the Walworth family had with that denomination.

It pained Clarence to think of Mansfield's seeking no consolation from the Church when he was in such a state of unrest, but he felt that perhaps he had been lax in not trying to counsel him more. However, Mansfield had been so antagonistic toward Clarence in the past few years that he probably would not have been able to help him. Clarence felt they must be thankful that Mansfield was at peace at last, since he certainly had had no inner peace for a very long time.

The murder trial began on June 25. Immediately, prominent lawyer friends of Reuben's took charge of Frank's defense. The threatening letters were read as evidence, and the New York Times called them "the ravings of a lunatic." The case created a sensation in the newspapers as one witness after another was called to the stand. The defense tried to prove Frank suffered from epileptic seizures, but the prosecution eroded the claim. The sensational trial ended with a sentence of life imprisonment.

As Frank was led out of the courtroom, Ellen went to his side with a face that tried to look cheerful, but with eyes that belied the attempt. She told him she would ride with him on the morrow on the train taking him to Sing-Sing and she clutched his arm with a desperate grip. She did accompany him and their sad farewell took place in the warden's office. Frank was put to work in the shoemaker's shop at the prison and within a month had lost fourteen pounds of weight. The day of his incarceration was the start of Ellen's campaign for his release.

A few months later, she received a letter from Frank, stating he was going to be transferred from Sing-Sing to the Auburn Insane Asylum and would be doing the same kind of work there. Ellen felt this would be the end of Frank's life if he had to stay in such a horrible place. She felt that fate had dealt her many heavy blows and wondered if she would ever be able to smile again.

Her mother, too, had passed away the year before, so she was more sad and lonely than ever, even though she had the love and support of her other children.

Ellen never ceased working through a network of acquaintances. After four years of unstinting effort, she obtained an executive pardon on August 14, 1877. Governor Lucius Robinson released Frank in what he called "one of the saddest chapters in the history of New York courts." Frank came home to Saratoga and the loving arms of those who awaited him at Pine Grove.

Chapter Twenty-Seven

♨

After Mansfield's death and Frank's imprisonment, Ellen knew she must find something to keep her every waking moment occupied. Even though she was doing everything in her power to secure Frank's release from prison, and she thought of him many times each day with a heavy heart, still she had to have some other outlet for her energies and emotions. Now that her children required less of her energies, she had more time to pursue her own intellectual interests.

By the middle of the nineteenth century, social influences were bringing change into human life, and feminist ideals were being brought to the fore by courageous women. They had begun breaking away from the stereotyped picture of the passive wife, silently following in the shadow of her husband. As decades passed, women's suffrage was being openly discussed and careers for women were being agitated. Women writers and editors were achieving fame, there were female lecturers on platforms across the nation, and nursing and stenography had become suitable pursuits. By 1870, a new independent, yet virtuous woman was emerging into the social strata. Ellen Walworth was at a place in her life where she was prepared to accept some of these new characteristics because of her religious and idealistic upbringing and her work in church and charity causes in the 1850s.

Ellen had given her own children the advantages of a first-class education. She did not look for another man to support her, but opened her own school after her divorce. She felt strongly that "Modern civilization made a demand upon women to go beyond the limits of family and social life." Of late, her thoughts and inclinations were never very far away from the lore that surrounded her at every turn in the Saratoga environs. She had long felt a pride in the pioneering accomplishments of both her own and her husband's ancestors. This pride could not linger buried forever without some form of expression.

Reubena was maturing into a loving and sensitive companion to her mother and the two often discussed the history of the area and also the stories within their own family. Reubena remembered very well the stories Ellen had told them as children about great-grandfather Benjamin Walworth and the part he took in the Revolutionary War battles as a member of General Washington's army in lower New York. Ellen's own great-grandfather, General John Hardin had also served right there at the battle of Saratoga, fighting with Morgan's Kentucky Rifle Corps. The Corps had held a very strategic position on the west side of the battlefield to prevent the escape of Burgoyne's troops. After the war, General Washington sent John Hardin under a flag of truce to make a treaty of peace with the Miami Indians in Ohio, where he had been cruelly massacred. Ellen's father had fought beside Abraham Lincoln in the Black Hawk War and had met his end in the Mexican War. There was a long history in the family of men who were willing to fight and die to make and preserve the nation, and Ellen felt a proud heritage.

Ellen had begun to feel a keen interest in the many Revolutionary War sites that were present all around her in Saratoga and she realized if action were not taken soon, they would be lost to the people forever. She knew too, she had to think of something beside her own troubles or she would surely lose her senses. Everything she had studied and read about the Revolutionary War had only served to spur her own desire to preserve the associations of that hallowed battleground and the memory of leaders who participated in those historic events.

The Saratoga Monument Association was chartered in 1859 for the purpose of erecting a suitable monument to commemorate the surrender of British forces to the Americans in October 1777. It became reactivated in 1872, after having its initial activities interrupted by the Civil War. The matter of erecting a suitable monument to commemorate Burgoyne's surrender and the importance of this triumph on the fortunes of the American struggle for independence were again being brought before the public. In 1874, the New York State Legislature granted an appropriation to commence the work, and the group issued an appeal to the patriotic people of New York, asking for financial aid to assist in the erection of this monument. Enough funds were not forthcoming to complete the task, but the committee raised enough to lay the foundation and cornerstone, together with a part of the base. This was located at the very spot where Burgoyne had his entrenched camp in the final days of the conflict and overlooked the flats beside the Hudson River where the surrender took place.

The reactivation of the monument committee and its pleas for funds aroused Ellen's latent historical sentiments. She cast about for a way to express them. Father Clarence, too, had always espoused an interest in history and genealogy, and Ellen often talked with him about the historical happenings of the region. One day when he was visiting the family at Saratoga, Ellen approached him with her idea of doing something definite that would help to spur an interest in the Revolutionary sites. She wanted to write something that would tell the story of the Battle of Saratoga for she felt there were not many people in the country who really knew much about that story. Also, with the fund drive of the Monument Committee, and the next year being the one hundredth anniversary of the battle, the times were right for publishing that story. She felt that historical subjects could not be claimed as belonging to only a small class of people. She wanted to make everyone proud of that period in history and to realize the impact it had on the making of the nation.

Clarence could not help but agree with her that there was a need to arouse the national conscience and spirit of patriotism. There was no doubt the Battle of Saratoga was considered one of the decisive military battles of the world, on a par with the defeat of the Spanish Armada or the surrender of Napoleon at Waterloo. The men who fought at Saratoga brought about a turn in the fortunes of the Americans and because of it, they received assistance from France and recognition by other foreign governments. He too felt that no one should underestimate the importance of this triumph on the American struggle for independence.

Ellen was much encouraged by Clarence's faith in her ability to tell the story and she decided to begin work on the project at once. She hoped what she would write would stimulate enough interest so that not just Saratoga, but every Revolutionary battlefield and site in the country could be marked in some way. She even thought some of the sites could become public parks, belonging to the government. She was so on fire with the idea that she was determined to find the time to do the project no matter how many other issues were pressing down on her.

She also confided to Clarence that she had been invited to make a fundraising speech at the Women's Pavilion at the Centennial Exposition in Philadelphia. A group of ladies were attempting to raise money in an effort to purchase and preserve Mount Vernon. They wanted to make it into a national shrine to the memory of General and Mrs. Washington.

Somehow, in spite of her school and her efforts for Frank, Ellen found the time she needed. In 1877, her monograph of the Battle of Saratoga and the campaign conducted by the Continental Army of 1777 was published and favorably received by the general public. The monograph detailed the battle and revealed how the overconfident British forces from Canada poured through the gateway of Champlain and Ticonderoga to sweep southward and meet their final fate in the picturesque region of Old Saratoga.

The very next year, the American News Company published her "Saratoga—The Battleground and Visitor's Guide." The booklet provided a guide and map of the battlefield and a description of the monument being erected. There was also a visitor's map and guide of Saratoga Springs. It listed the twenty-five famous mineral springs that were the treasure and pride of the little city, as well as short walks and drives to be taken in the surrounding countryside.

Hotels and boarding houses were also mentioned, as well as the library, schools, medical institutions, and sanitaria. The large hotels were described as being among the finest in the world. Their broad piazzas faced Broadway and swept around inner courts with beautiful lawns, cooling fountains and magnificent shade trees. Each hotel had its own band and provided music for balls, hops, and morning Germans, a dance of intricate figures. The elite of the entire country met at the United States Hotel during "the season" with two thousand guests being the norm.

Ellen's "Visitor's Guide" was incorporated into the articles deposited within the cornerstone of the monument at Schuylerville at its laying on October 17, 1877. She and her family were invited and honored guests at the affair. An elaborate patriotic celebration was held to commemorate the occasion, with the Masonic fraternity from all over New York gathered, as well as military organizations from New York and New England and many prominent persons from other states as well. A two-mile procession marched through the streets of the little village of Schuylerville to the monument, where the cornerstone was laid by the Grand Master of the New York Masonic Order, before an audience of thirty thousand people. Poems, commemorative orations, and addresses were delivered from two grandstands.

The completion of the monument proved to be a titanic struggle and the committee met with many disappointments. At last, sufficient money was appropriated to complete the structure over the objections of many narrow-minded legislators. The monument proved to be a tribute not only to the victory of American arms but to the indomitable perseverance of the members of the Association. The view from the apex of the monument was superb, but to quote Ellen Walworth: "It is not because of the scenery—hill and dale, sparkling water, beauteous wood, ethereal vault of blue, and misty mountains of enchantment—that this locality allures and holds the vagrant vision. This monument is the cynosure of patriotism."

Ellen's place in the community as a member of a leading family, her intense interest in history and education, and her book commemorating the battle, led to her appointment as a member of the Saratoga Monument Committee in 1878, at a meeting of that group held at the United States Hotel. She was the only woman member of the board at that time. She found herself plunged into a round of civic, educational and historical activities, often daring to pioneer as the first woman member. At her first meeting as a member of the Monument Association board, at the request of Governor Horatio Seymour, she made an appeal for permanently marking the points of interest on the battlefield at Bemis Heights. A resolution was passed to secure memorial stones to be inscribed and placed at these points, and Ellen was named chairman of that committee. In a later report she commented: "I have been busy with my committee duties and after consulting military and other maps, have found nineteen historical places that must be marked as soon as possible. I have contacted many of the property owners upon whose lands these markers will be placed. I am pleased to report that everyone has been most cooperative. I am already going out among my friends and acquaintances, soliciting gifts of money for these tablets and their placement. These tablets will give emphasis to the memories connected with the field of battle. We have already had many generous responses. Needless to say, I have made innumerable trips to the site with my horse and carriage and in fact, I do not believe we even have to guide the steed anymore. He knows that as we head out toward Saratoga Lake, we are on our way to the battleground."

"I have also contacted my brother in Chicago, General Martin D. Hardin. He will give a tablet to commemorate the services of our great-grandfather, Colonel John Hardin, of Morgan's Rifle Corps. The architect of our monument, Mr. Jared Clark Markham, will also give a tablet in honor of his own Revolutionary ancestor from Connecticut."

One day in the fall of 1883, Ellen invited a small group to meet at Pine Grove to form an organization with the lengthy title of "The Historical Society of Saratoga, including the Upper Hudson, Lake George and Lake Champlain." Ellen Hardin Walworth was the only female member of the original board of trustees.

Chapter Twenty-Eight

ᶜℐᵖ

Shortly after Frank had come home from the prison at Auburn, he and Ellen sat down to a serious talk about what the future might hold for him. Ellen felt it might be wiser if Frank left Saratoga as he had already encountered some cruel snubs from people whom they had thought were their friends. Frank's health was not good, he had a bad cough and the cold winters in northern New York probably would not be the best for that condition. While Ellen hated to see Frank go away, she reminded him that he could always come back for visits or forever and that Pine Grove would always be his home.

Frank, for his part, had also spent some time trying to make new plans for his life and he agreed that Saratoga did not look appealing at the moment. He did not feel he could successfully open a law practice there. Also, there were too many memories of the family and what he had done to it with his impetuous actions. He told his mother he would get in touch with his Uncle Lemuel in Kentucky. He hoped there might still be some connections there that would be helpful to him in starting a new life.

Ellen thought this a sensible idea and even agreed that when he went, she would take a little trip down there also to revisit old family territory, for she would always have a special place in her heart for Kentucky and the many memories it brought to mind. Now that Nelly was teaching in Ellen's school, it was possible for her to get away for awhile.

Lemuel and Frank's friends were contacted and within a short time a letter was received, encouraging Frank to come back to Louisville. Ellen began packing bags for the journey and she and Frank set out in a more lighthearted frame of mind than they had experienced in many a year. Upon their arrival, Ellen helped Frank find a suite of rooms in a comfortable house and soon he was well settled in .

Ellen reminded Frank that in a way he was "coming home" when he came back to Kentucky. She told him of the wonderful memories of her grandmother Hardin whom she went to see often when she was a little girl. Ellen remembered she had had a grand farm and very handsome house at Frankfort, but when her son went to settle in Illinois, she broke up her establishment and followed him. She built a large house there with lovely grounds and gardens and had a large stable for horses. It was there that Ellen learned to ride. Ellen recalled that her grandmother had black hair and sparkling black eyes, even at seventy-five years of age. Even though she was a staunch Calvinist, she gave wonderful cotillions and served sumptuous suppers. Ellen had always regarded her grandmother as a wonderful example of womanhood.

Knowing her school in Saratoga would soon require her presence and seeing Frank was securely ensconced in his new location and seemed happy with the move, Ellen shortly thereafter boarded the train for the North.

The two older girls, Nelly and Clara, were growing to mature womanhood. Their careers were a matter of concern to Ellen. In her preoccupation with Frank and securing his release from prison, she had sometimes felt pangs of guilt that she was not giving them the attention they deserved. However, they seemed to understand and be patient with her in those trying times. After Nelly's graduation from Kenwood, she had pursued a teaching career, coming back to Pine Grove to assist Ellen in the management of the school there and this pleased her mother very much. The same could not be said with respect to the vocation that Clara chose to pursue in 1881.

Reubena came into the library one day with a note in her hand, saying she had found this note for Ellen laying on the threshold to the door of Clara's room. A look of dismay flushed Ellen's face as she read the note that said she had gone to the convent at Kenwood and planned to remain there and pursue studies toward taking her vows as a nun, and that no one was to follow her there for her avowal was definite. Ellen read the letter to Reubena and declared she would be at that convent at an early hour the next day for she felt Clara did not fully realize the implications of such a drastic step.

Reubena in turn tried to reason with her mother, reminding her that Clara had always been a serious girl and that she must believe what she was doing was right. She also reminded her mother that Nelly and Clara had spent a lot of time with Uncle Clarence, and that Ellen had always felt that was all right.

Ellen's temper now suddenly rose at that thought and she felt she had been lax in allowing them to spend so much time at the rectory with Clarence. She felt he had probably been talking church vocation with them for years. She recalled she had converted to Catholicism under Clarence's influence when she was young and full of idealistic motives. She had felt the Catholic religion would procure liberty for her to become the person she thought she wanted to be, but instead she had found it to be a trap full of superstition, and her own faith in that church had long since withered. Now she deeply regretted the day she ever left the Episcopal Church and she feared she had brought this catastrophe on her own child by her silly foolhardiness. She now saw she should never have allowed the girls to spend so much time in Albany under Clarence's protective wing. She could not help but feel that to become a nun would be a dreadful waste of Clara's talents and that she would be ensnared within the convent. The next morning, Ellen was at the Sacred Heart convent, where she demanded her daughter be handed back to her. In tears, Clara rode the train home to Saratoga while Ellen berated her for being an impressionistic child and vented her own bitterness in tears that matched Clara's.

While Ellen could not readily forget what Clara had done, she had just begun to make peace with herself when a new crisis came along to cause her further grief. The door opened one day to disclose Mansfield Tracy Walworth, Ellen's second son and fourth living child. She had supposed that Tracy was busily pursuing his studies at medical school, but here he was on the doorstep. Coming into the house, he told his mother that even though school was still in session, he was not going back and in fact he was not going anywhere, he was staying right there at Pine Grove if that met with Ellen's approval. He said he needed some peace and quiet and some time for himself for he did not feel very well. He never did like having to meet new people and be nice to them when it cost him such an effort. He said he knew his mother had told him he would feel differently when he was older, but he did not, and college did not seem to have made any difference either. He hated being so far away from home and from everything that was familiar to him. That was the reason he had left Georgetown University and come back to Schenectady to attend Union College. He did not know where he ever got the idea he wanted to be a doctor even though he liked science well enough. He wanted to stay home and just try to be a help to his mother and not go out into the world of competition.

Ellen tried to hide her distress at this turn of events and the fearful thought crossed her mind that Tracy was sounding just like his father! She had felt for some time that Tracy was the one child who showed a touch of Mansfield's instability and it was ironic this one should also be his namesake. By the time Tracy reached adolescence she noticed he never seemed to be able to adjust to its trial or pleasures, but was always fighting his own inner battles. He often shut himself in his room with a book instead of going out to the playing fields with the other boys. Competition had seemed to overwhelm him and he retreated from it. He had been a good scholar and had chosen Georgetown for his college because Frank had gone there. Before long, however, his old problems of adjustment cropped up, and he wrote his mother that he wanted to transfer to Union College so he could be closer to home. When he decided to enter medical school, it came as a surprise to her.

Her heart felt very heavy as she reviewed Tracy's past. She was struck with the terrifying thought that he might be heading in the direction Mansfield had taken, although he showed none of Mansfield's eccentric or arrogant behavior. Suddenly she realized what she had not seen before. She knew now that Tracy would never be able to face up to the stern demands of real life, but would always be introverted and feeling unwell. It was like a crushing weight on her chest, but she spoke evenly as she told Tracy he would always have a home at Pine Grove and that they did need a man's assistance with the care of the property. She also reminded him he could be a friend to Reubena who was often alone because of Ellen's school and civic demands. Ellen wondered in her heart if she had been so busy with her community endeavors that she had not been responsive to the needs of her loved ones and said as much to Tracy.

Tracy patted Ellen's clenched hand and told her not to reproach herself for he marveled at the strength and determination she had and wished he could be the same way, but he knew he never would. With that, he picked up his bags in the hall and turned toward the stairs that led up to his bedroom.

Chapter Twenty-Nine

୶

O ne day in 1881, Ellen opened a letter that came to her at Saratoga Springs. It was an invitation to go to Yorktown, Virginia, for a celebration there that would commemorate the one-hundredth anniversary of Washington's victory over Cornwallis in 1781. Ellen felt she must have received this invitation because of her activities with the Saratoga Monument Association and her efforts to place markers at points of interest on the Saratoga battlefield. She was busily immersed in trying to identify all the spots where the markers should be, studying old maps and walking over farmer's fields and getting property owners to agree to the placement of certain tablets on their land. Probably the hardest job of all was contacting people who might be interested in donating a marker in honor of their own Revolutionary War ancestor who fought at Saratoga. She had even convinced Governor Seymour of New York to give one in honor of his ancestor. Not knowing how she could spare the time to attend the program but eager to go nevertheless, she sought out Reubena to tell her of the invitation. Reubena felt it was too tempting an offer not to accept and urged her mother to go. Ellen surprised Reubena by saying she would like her to take the trip with her, and that it would do them both good to have a change of scene. The timetables were soon looked over to see what connections could be made from Saratoga to Washington and then on to Yorktown.

Ellen felt tremendous consolation from the fact that there seemed to be some real interest evolving in the deeds of the founders of the nation. Just three years ago, in 1878, the sentiments of Congress had been aroused by the demand of many interested persons to commemorate all of the Revolutionary battlefields. Congress had also voted the sum of thirty-thousand dollars to finish the monument at Schuylerville, so Ellen could not help but feel all of her efforts had not been in vain and important historic sites were not going to be lost.

As she looked over the remainder of the day's mail, however, a frown came over her face and she complained to Reubena that she guessed they must take drastic action if they were to survive the year without ending up in debtors' prison. It sometimes seemed as if every morning, Ellen had to face a mountain standing in her path and she wondered if they would ever be in a secure financial position again. She never realized how lucrative the Chancellor's law practice had been until it was gone and she could not help but feel a twinge of remorse that Mansfield did not settle into it and then they might have avoided all the trials that seemed to have beset them at every turn. The burden of providing a home for her family had rested on her for such a long time and she did wish it could have been just a little easier to bear. She mentioned to Reubena that perhaps she should plan to open the house that summer to boarders from the city in an effort to make ends meet.

That fall found Ellen supervising a project that had crept into her thoughts often during the past few months. Standing amid the dust and debris of the ripped-out partitions and sawdust from new timbers used to renovate the Walworth homestead, Ellen pondered the changes and additions that would make the old home into a comfortable lodging for paying guests who would come to spend the summer months in Saratoga. She was already looking forward to having among her first guests the former Union governor of Kentucky, Thomas E. Bramlette and his family.

Clara came up the walk and wrinkled her nose at all the commotion. She reminded her mother that Grandfather Walworth was probably turning over in his grave at this renovation of his beloved old home and she could not help but wonder where the family was going to stay when the house was full of paying guests.

Ellen assured her it would be perfectly logical for the family to take over the carriage house in the rear for the summer and that her carpenter was going to partition off a few bedrooms in that building. In the winter, they would move back into the main house.

Clara announced to her mother that she hoped not to be around much longer to have to put up with all of the inconvenience and rearrangement. She had not made any plans as yet, but when she did it would not include Saratoga. She also told her mother she would not be a burden to her in the way of expending money for her support.

Ellen reminded Clara she was no more privileged than the rest of the family to be inconvenienced and that these rearrangements were quite necessary if they were to carry on in a financial way as the school did not bring in enough money to support them, even with the two girls teaching there.

Ellen changed the subject to that of their old friends from

Kentucky, the Bramlettes. She asked Clara if she remembered their visiting Bird's Nest and how Frank seemed even then to have a soft spot in his heart for their daughter and tried to cover it up with teasing and boyish pranks. Ellen hoped that when the Bramlettes were with them in the summer that Clara, Nelly, and Reubena, too would pay some attention to young Corinne and help to make her visit there as pleasant as possible.

The Bramlettes were visitors not only in 1882 but in the summer of 1883 as well and Frank was in attendance at Saratoga each time. He suggested to his mother that Corinne be invited to share Thanksgiving with the Walworths that November. Returning to Kentucky with Corinne, Frank wrote his mother a letter within a few days. When Reubena brought the letter to her mother in the schoolroom, she wondered if the letter contained some information about Corinne Bramlette and she could not help mentioning it to her mother.

Ellen, on her part, had a moment of hesitation as she thought of some young woman taking away a part of Frank's affection. She had always held a special place in her own heart for this beloved son who had taken such a burden on himself to avenge the wrongs that life had dealt to her. The idea of giving up a part of his affections to another woman did not sit kindly upon her. However, she answered Reubena that indeed the letter was mostly about Corinne, with Frank saying he had been in love with her since he first met her in 1872, when she was a girl of seventeen. He had carried the memory of her in his heart for many years, but never dared think himself worthy of her, especially after what happened with the shooting and prison term. The renewed acquaintance for the past two summers in Saratoga had made him press his suit, and Corinne was as eager to accept him as he was to marry her. Ellen reflected on the fact that Corinne was twenty-eight and Frank was thirty, so it was not as if they were silly youngsters falling in love and that since Corrine seemed a very sensible person, she would probably be well suited to Frank.

Ellen quietly put the letter aside and gazed at Reubena's animated face, realizing quite suddenly that the girl was no longer her baby, but was growing into a very pretty young woman. Ellen realized too that Reubena's position as a favorite of everyone in the family would predict that friendship and love would come to her easily. In all likelihood, this sweet sixteen-year-old would someday bring home a suitor who would come to take Reubena away from Ellen. She sighed as she told Reubena that Frank said in his letter he wanted to be married at Pine Grove on December 20.

Chapter Thirty

✑

The day after Frank's wedding, Clara packed her bags and told her mother she had made her decision about what to do with her life. Nothing anyone could say or do would sway her. She left for the convent at Kenwood and because of the bitterness of the parting, did not see her mother for more than a year. In March 1884, Ellen went once again to Kenwood and pleaded with Clara to return home, but Clara was adamant in her refusal.

Ellen was convinced it was Father Clarence who had cajoled and persuaded Clara into this course of action. She could not help but feel he had taken from her one of her own children and made her into what his wishes would be for his own daughter if he had ever sired one. She ranted that he was a scoundrel, not a saint at all, despite what his parishioners thought of him and that she at least knew the black side of him and never wanted to be in his presence again. Nothing that Clarence could do now would ever make Ellen forgive him for what he had done to her in influencing Clara's conduct.

Clara, in her turn, admonished her mother against saying such evil things about Father Clarence. She reminded her that he did all he could for Ellen when Grandfather Walworth died and she was separated from their father and in need of money. It was Clarence who insisted that a portion of Mansfield's inheritance be paid to Ellen for the support of her children. It was he who had stood by and assisted in every way he could when Frank was on trial and in prison. He had taken Nelly to Europe and paid a lot of attention to both Nelly and Clara at a time when Ellen was busy with other things. Clara reminded her mother that she certainly had been influenced in her vocation by Father Clarence and begged her mother to remember that he influenced her once too, and that she became a Catholic because of it.

Clara insisted that both Father Clarence and the nuns at the convent tried very hard to make sure the girls had a genuine desire to give their lives to the Church and were not on some emotional enthusiasm. She reiterated that she was not insincere in her choice and that she wanted to become a nun and teach art, just as she did at her mother's school. She said again that her mind was made up and nothing Ellen could do or say would change it.

Ellen told Clara if she went into the convent it would not be with her blessing, but she was sure Clara would be successful in whatever course she chose because she was a bright and conscientious girl. Ellen still thought it was too demanding a life for such a lovely young person to assume and she vowed she would never, never, forgive Clarence Walworth for what he had done. Ellen was absent, but Clarence was present, when Clara took the veil in July 1884.

Six months had now passed since Frank and Corinne were married. Summer of 1884 saw them back at Pine Grove, where they decided to make their home. Frank told Ellen he had missed being near his family in Saratoga and he really did not have an inclination to pursue his law career further. He wanted to teach in Ellen's school and felt that would give him time for writing poetry, which he dearly loved.

A dreadful pang of remembrance swept through Ellen and she felt a cold ache in her stomach. How much these statements sounded like a young Mansfield! How ironic that Frank had inherited some of the same tendencies of his hated father. She had feared for some time that Frank had little ambition to make a success of a career, but she had buried those thoughts behind excuses for the trials that had beset him in adult life and the poor state of his health since he had been in prison. Now she hid her fears and told Frank how happy they would all be to have him and Corinne as a part of the family again. Now that Clara had left, she could use him in the school.

Saratoga Springs was increasing steadily in its attraction for summer visitors. In 1885, the household was again in a state of upheaval as Ellen made complete alterations to Pine Grove. She hired J. C. Markham, the architect who had designed the Saratoga Monument, to make a sweeping renovation and addition. The building was expanded to fifty-five rooms and given the newly fashionable Queen Anne facade that completely obliterated the simply designed house of 1815. Pine Grove was renamed "The Walworth Mansion" and became a small family-style Saratoga hotel, offering comfortable accommodations at reasonable prices.

In the midst of all the renovations, a new life was also quickening in Corinne and in March 1886, a daughter, Clara Grant, was born to Frank and Corinne. At the time, Ellen had no reason to believe this tiny babe would be her only grandchild. In the summer season, the rooms of The Walworth Mansion were full of visitors enjoying the waters, the ambiance, and the cool mountain air of the little city. The fall term of school had just opened when Frank came down the stairs one morning to announce he had a sore throat and a general feeling of malaise. As the days went by, Frank's condition did not respond to medication or even the old-fashioned mustard plaster applied to his chest and back by Ellen's loving hands. Coughing racked his thin body and Ellen could hear his struggles for breath echoing down the hallway. The doctor was summoned and called the case "acute bronchitis."

Ellen lay awake at night listening to the racking coughs and when she finally slept, it was a sleep punctuated by sad and frightful dreams. Suddenly she awoke with a start, realizing she had been sleeping, and she was not now aware of any coughing. Putting on her wrapper, she tiptoed to Frank's room where all was quiet in the light of early dawn. A premonition made her go over to the bed and when she did she uttered a piercing scream. She held the inert body of Frank in her arms as she shrieked for the others to come quickly. In a torrent of hysterical tears, Ellen cried that her Frank was dead and another of her children had been taken from her. The mourning clothes came out of the closet again and Frank was laid to rest at the age of thirty-three, his little daughter too young to ever know her father. Ellen was in a state of deep depression for months over this latest blow, but life had to go on. She tried to busy herself with the school and her family, but existed in a state of numb awareness of each passing day.

When the school year was finally over, Ellen called Nelly into the parlor for a serious reassessment with regard to it. She did not feel, since Frank was gone, that she could face the effort involved to keep the school going. It had been in operation for sixteen years and she no longer saw it as a challenge, but rather as a terrible burden that she could no longer carry. Even running

the house as a summer hotel seemed like a formidable challenge
and she was so bone-tired and heartsick that she felt she was
ready for a change of scene. She felt she needed to get far away
from Saratoga and all the scenes of sorrow she had endured
there.

She told Nelly she had already been inquiring about leasing
The Walworth Mansion to someone who would run it for her in
the summer. She would also send a letter to her pupils' parents,
advising them that the school would be permanently closed.
Reubena was studying at Vassar, so she could live with Ellen
when she was not in school. She thought Tracy would stay
around the place as a watchman and handyman to see it was
kept safe from harm, as she had no wish to sell it. With Clara in
the convent, there was only Nelly to make a decision as to what
she would want to do now that there was no teaching job at
home for her.

Nelly at once assured her mother she too was ready for new
challenges. She told Ellen that even though she knew how much
Ellen hated Clarence, she would go to Albany and try to find a
teaching job there, and she was sure Clarence would be able to
help her with that. She herself could never forget all of his kind-
ness to her and Clara and it was her frequent visits to see them
both that had sustained her in all the long, sad months. She said
she had become quite fond of Corinne and baby Clara and that
since Corinne had no desire to go back to Kentucky, she would
consider taking them to Albany with her.

Before too many weeks had passed, Nelly had secured a
teaching position in Albany and taken an apartment there.
Clarence was more than happy to have another member of his
family near him again. Corinne and the baby moved into the
apartment with Nelly. The big house on Broadway in Saratoga

Springs was practically deserted for the first time in its history.

On a fall day in 1889, Tracy was raking up leaves on the front lawn when his mother came to tell him that he would be in charge of The Walworth Mansion now for she had taken an apartment in Washington, D.C. for the winter. She said she would be coming up to Saratoga in the "season" for she had always enjoyed the festivities at that time. Reubena had now graduated from Vassar and taken a position at the U.S. Patent Office in Washington, and if Ellen moved there, they could see more of one another. However, she reminded Tracy that Saratoga would always be their permanent home for this was where the Walworths had established themselves.

On New Year's Day 1890, Ellen looked out of her apartment window at the Langham Hotel in Washington and saw the sun shining on the bare branches of the trees across the street. it looked like a promise of fair weather for the day. Ellen wrote in her journal that she hoped "it was a sign for fair promise for the next decade."

Chapter Thirty-One

⤜⤛

Ellen was not inactive over the winter in Washington. She was soon making inroads into the circles of influence in the Capital, partly because of her family and social connections in both Saratoga and Kentucky. The Victorian Age was quietly passing from the scene and Ellen, always the epitome of the devoted matriarch, seemed somehow to be ahead of her time when civic action was required. She was an active social feminist and was just beginning to feel the full thrust of her powers in this direction. She felt, "Love of country is but the development of the love of family and home. As woman is supreme in the home, so in the development of national life, she is destined to become a factor, if not a guide, in the affairs of the nation."

She and Reubena were taking New Year's Day dinner with Mary Desha, a long-standing acquaintance from Lexington, Kentucky, who had come to Washington in 1885 when her brother was elected to Congress. Mary and Ellen shared many similar views about the role of women in society and also the need for patriotic fervor among the American people.

Over dessert and coffee, Mary declaimed on the flood of immigrants coming into America and the fact that she felt they would pose a threat to American institutions. Her brother had told her the booming industries were exerting power on Congress to ease the immigration laws so that more workers could be brought into the country to work in the textile and steel mills.

Ellen countered with the fact that most of the immigrants were from the eastern and southern countries of Europe and they were highly illiterate and would congregate in their own ethnic communities where the language barrier did not matter. Therefore, she felt many of them never would learn to speak English and could not be assimilated into the American culture.

Mary Desha shifted in her chair and warmed to the subject, in agreement with Ellen. She could not see how these people could ever have any conception of the principles of democratic government that the founding fathers worked so hard to implant in the American mind. She felt that somehow these immigrants must be made Americans, and soon, or the native population would be inundated, with the American culture swallowed up and stamped out. While the outlook of these women was short-sighted, still they were the product of their own time and circumstance and they were frightened of losing their American ideal.

Ellen agreed with Mary that someone must join forces to resist the dangers of inundation by the foreigners. She felt a link with the past would promote the nation's history for all people of the country to see and understand. Someone must be the guardians of the form of government set up by the founding fathers and become stewards of the constitution. She thoroughly agreed with Mary that those who had been in America for centuries should be the ones to promote these ideals, for the new settlers to our shores could know nothing of what had transpired in the past.

Mary called Ellen's attention to the fact that America's

centennial year of 1876 really got the public to thinking on these matters and have a new respect for the principles of democratic government. The very impressive display of colonial relics at the exposition at Philadelphia had made Mary dream of preserving the past so there would be traditions to hand down to one's children. She also felt it could set an example to the newcomers if they could know and see a part of the heritage of America.

Ellen spoke of the founding of the Sons of the American Revolution just a few short months ago. Their purpose was to do the very things Ellen and Mary had been speaking of. Since they were a male organization, that would leave the women to do something on their own if only they could find a way in which to do it. Always the mother, Ellen felt the role in society that had always been played by mother love fostering the dream of the ideal patriotic American home should be stressed in any project the women might undertake.

In July of that year of 1890, a letter appeared in the Washington Post, written by Mrs. Mary Smith Lockwood and addressed to William McDowell, the founding president of the Sons of the American Revolution. Mrs. Lockwood stated she was in complete agreement with the society's aim to preserve the sacred honor and records of men who served in the American Revolution. Then she asked where the courageous women of the same war should be given a roll of honor, since the SAR did not allow women to belong to their society, even though they had been invited as observers to the founding meeting.

William McDowell took up Mrs. Lockwood's challenge, and urged in the papers that women should form their own society to preserve the memory of their Revolutionary ancestors. He sent a copy of the SAR constitution and application blanks, along with other pertinent information, to spur Mrs. Lockwood into action.

Both Mrs. Lockwood and Mary Desha were activists. Mary Desha lost no time in contacting Mary Lockwood when she saw the letter in the Post. Before long the two had met and drawn up a list of friends who might be interested and eligible to follow the suggestions made by McDowell.

Mary Desha promptly stated: "We must put on our list the name of Miss Eugenia Washington. After all, she is a descendent of General Washington, so there can be no doubt of her patriotic leanings. She is a well-known figure in the area and a lady of means, so she would be a great asset to our cause. Then too, put down the name of Ellen Hardin Walworth, an acquaintance of mine originally from Kentucky, but living here in the Capital now. She is from a fine old family and her ancestor fought with Morgan's Rifle Corps. She has been living in Saratoga for years at the Walworth family home and in so doing, she became very inspired to preserve the memories of the American Revolution at the Saratoga battlefield. She even wrote a booklet about the battleground. It was so impressive that Saratoga Monument Association made her the first woman member to serve on the Saratoga Board of Education, and as a woman of refinement, as well as prominent lineage, she would certainly be desirable. I will speak to her about this matter right away."

Mary Desha lost no time in approaching Ellen and they decided to set up a meeting on August 9 for the interested women to be held at Ellen's apartment in the Langham Hotel. The afternoon of the meeting there was a severe thunderstorm, so only Mary Desha and Eugenia Washington were present. Mary Desha had brought with her a packet of materials from the SAR, sent to Mrs. Lockwood by Mr. McDowell.

Ellen remarked to the ladies that the Elks, Shriners, Odd Fellows and even the Veteran's associations all had a feminine counterpart affiliated with their organizations. She could not understand why the SAR did not want an auxiliary, but since they did not seem to, she supposed that the women must found their own independent patriotic society.

Miss Washington was sorting through the papers and forms from the SAR and she felt they needed to look it all over carefully and then proceed along the same guidelines. She felt as strongly as Ellen did that if the women of American did not band together to protect the native heritage she feared they would lose it and all that General Washington and his men had suffered and died for during those terrible days at Valley Forge, Bunker Hill, Yorktown, and elsewhere.

Again Ellen said: "The American home is where these ideals must be inculcated. Even though I have had many unhappy experiences in my own family, they have not swayed my belief that the mother must be the guide and motivating factor in educating her children in the principles of their inheritance as American citizens. An interest in patriotism and history, a love of country, should be an extension of family love. In that way, woman is a factor and guide in the affairs of the nation."

With this philosophy in mind, the three women studiously examined the papers that Mary Desha had brought. They appointed a number of officers, including themselves, from the list that Lockwood and Desha had compiled earlier.

On October 11, 1890 another meeting attended by most of the women designated as officers, was held to be the official founding date of what was to become the most influential patriotic society organized for women—the Daughters of the American Revolution. Its founding members pledged themselves to "protect historic sites and records, preserve the national archives, sponsor peace and arbitration among nations, give citizenship help to the foreign born, preserve the gravesites of Revolutionary War soldiers, and encourage historical research, as well as perpetuate the memory of Revolutionary War heroes and heroines." Its "Home and Country" motto was a formula for success in the nativistic, class-conscience reaction to changes in the social structure that had occurred during the last decades of the nineteenth century. The group also determined that only a woman of national prominence must be first president. Mrs. Benjamin Harrison, wife of the nation's twenty-third President, accepted the honor.

The Daughters of the American Revolution had come into being in large measure due to the efforts of Ellen Hardin Walworth. In 1891, the Saratoga Monument Association sent cordial wishes for success in their patriotic undertakings to the Daughters of the American Revolution. It was a gesture of honor and respect for one of their own board members who had gone on to become a co-founder of this national society.

Chapter Thirty-Two

❦

E llen was now fifty-four years of age. The traces of her many sadnesses and disappointments in life could be found in her eyes and on her somber countenance. However, the basic philosophy that she had carried with her from that first train ride from Kentucky to the new home in Saratoga Springs was still a part of her personality. That philosophy she expressed as "I am determined not only to hold my own, but to make myself felt in the community to which I belong. . . and I believe I will succeed."

Ellen stayed on in Washington and one day she told Reubena that she had received an invitation that promised to be most exciting. She had been asked to speak before the American Historical Association at the Chicago World's Fair. The "Daughters" had been prospering and growing so much in membership for over three years that the Historical Association seemed to feel they had something worthwhile to tell their audience.

Reubena was enthusiastic about the invitation and she also proposed that she be allowed to accompany her mother to Chicago. They would take a few extra days and tour the exhibits, since Reubena had never been to a World's Fair.

Ellen was delighted that Reubena wished to go with her and she said she already knew what she would speak about to the Historical Association. Since she had been in Washington and had access to some of the government offices, she had seen valuable and historical papers and pictures scattered hither and yon among the records. She felt these should be preserved and put in one central office in Washington for they were papers and pictures that belonged to the people of the country and formed a part of the national heritage. She would propose to the American Historical Association that some kind of national archives be established to take care of these important documents.

Reubena could readily see her mother had another "cause" toward which to bend her energies. She never seemed without some good work to pursue in spite of all the hard work she had done all her life in raising a family of five children and having so many disasters accompany that family. Ellen knew that she always wanted to have something to look forward to, to challenge her mind and energies. She needed that now even more since she had lost so much of her family.

Reubena had left the Patent Office job in Washington to return to the Art Students League in New York, but she often visited her mother in Washington. Ellen knew where her remaining family was in a physical sense, but she still felt she had lost them—lost four children to death; Clara to the Nunnery; Nelly to Clarence's influence and Tracy to a deficient personality. Reubena was her only intellectual companion now for she realized that things were changing rapidly in the world and Reubena had, with her, a genuine desire for women to take their proper place in society. Even with Reubena's suffragist activities, she was still her mother's "little Puritan" in her sweet, simple tastes and unassuming manner. Ellen felt her other children had all grown away from her and did not return the love she bore for them.

Reubena urged her mother not to grieve so for the others for they were happy in what they were doing. Clara had become a fine art teacher, Nelly seemed very happy living next door to Clarence and acting as his secretary now that his eyesight was failing so rapidly. The house that he had bought for Nelly also made a home for Corinne and little Clara and they were indispensable to Uncle Clarence in his old age. Even Tracy, although he was only a handyman around their place in Saratoga, seemed happy in being there. He was helping Clarence with some Walworth genealogy and was finding his fulfillment in his own way. Reubena urged her mother to come to New York and live with her for she felt her mother's major work in Washington was finished.

When they returned from Chicago, Ellen made the move to New York. The year 1896 found her studying law at New York University, in a course taught to familiarize non-professional women with legal principles that could affect their daily lives. The offshoot of this study course was to popularize the study of law by women. Every summer saw Reubena and Ellen embarked for an extended stay at the Walworth Mansion in Saratoga, where Reubena conducted sketching classes. In 1894, Reubena had given up her painting studio at West 57th Street in New York and returned to Vassar, to graduate with a Bachelor of Arts degree in 1896 at the age of twenty-nine.

Already the clouds of national crisis portended trouble with Spain over an insignificant island located off the tip of Florida. The business interests which put refined white sugar on American tables were disturbed that Spain could not maintain a stable government in the island of Cuba. Ten years of war between the mother country and its possession had brought only hatred, bloodshed, and repressive cruelty. The Americans who had invested in Cuba found that Spain was unable to protect their rights. Early in 1898, the U.S. battleship Maine was sent to the harbor of Havana to protect American interests. The slogan "Remember the Maine" would ring through the national consciousness in the next few months and place not only America but the Walworths as well in a precarious position.

Chapter Thirty-Three

cᴏ

O n the morning of February 16, 1898, Reubena bundled herself well against the cold winds of winter and started down the stairs of her apartment house for the private school where she was a teacher. Within minutes she came rushing back to tell her mother the news that the Maine had been sunk in Havana harbor with a fearful loss of life.

It certainly looked as if Spain was asking for war in doing such a dastardly action. People were already calling upon President McKinley to declare war against Spain. Ellen on her part, could not help but shed a tear over the situation for she could not forget how horrible a war could be. She told Reubena of those dreadful times in the Civil War when after every battle people would pray for days that their loved one's name would not be on the casualty lists. Living in Kentucky as she did she spent many sleepless nights wondering if raiding parties would break down the doors in search of food and supplies, and there were many bad moments when both Martin and Lemuel were wounded. She certainly did not want to think of going to war again, but she knew if it came there was nothing that people could do but help the government in whatever way they could to bring it to a quick and successful conclusion.

The Maine was sunk in February. By April, President McKinley had bowed to the popular opinion to liberate the Cubans from "Spanish tyranny" and avenge the sinking. He came before Congress, seeking authority to end the civil war in Cuba. That body, on April 21st, declared a state of war—demanding Spain's withdrawal from Cuba and authorizing the President of the United States to use the army and naval forces to achieve that end.

A few weeks later, Reubena approached her mother and stated that with the whole country putting forth every effort to win the war, she wanted to do her part too in a more active fashion than writing letters to soldiers or rolling bandages. Reubena reminded her mother there were no boys in the Walworth family to go to war and fight for the country as there had been in all the wars before. She felt that she, Reubena, must be the one to represent the Walworth family in the conflict.

Ellen could not imagine what Reubena would do in an active way to help the war effort but she soon found that the girl had already made plans. She had decided to be a nurse and take a quick course in nursing. She had already written to the hospital at Saratoga and they would take her into an intensive course so that she would be ready to serve in just a couple of months. She planned to go up there right away and get started.

This news took Ellen completely by surprise. Reubena told her mother she had had all the communications about her project sent to her at school because she wanted her secret to be her own until she knew if she would be accepted.

Ellen realized that she had not been paying much attention to Reubena's actions since she had become so busy with her own. President McKinley had asked the National Society of the Daughters of the American Revolution to recruit nurses and Ellen had been commuting to Washington in her volunteer role as Director General of the Women's National War Relief Association. She realized that Reubena had had ample opportunity for her schemes to escape her mother's notice. Little had Ellen thought that she might actually be recruiting her own daughter!

Within a few days, Reubena took the train to Saratoga for her training. Within two months, she was sent to Fortress Monroe in Virginia, where she was nursing, but not the wounded soldiers she so desperately hoped to care for. Meanwhile, Ellen had been sent to Camp Wyckoff on Long Island, where she went to work as the representative of the Women's National War Relief Association. The government had opened a new hospital there to receive wounded men, and the need for nurses occupied Ellen in continuing her recruiting and also allotting and accounting for supplies. She kept in touch with Reubena by letters, writing of the critical need for nurses at Montauk and of the inadequacies of Camp Wyckoff. This information did not fall on deaf ears at Fortress Monroe.

Reubena felt that it was only right that she give her work at the place where it was most needed and there was adequate staff on hand at her present post. She applied for a transfer to go to Camp Wyckoff and began counting the days until she could be with her mother.

Ellen read her letter with dismay and immediately replied, trying her best to dissuade Reubena from coming to the barren, windswept, and poorly equipped camp. However, she did close the latter by saying that if it was really Reubena's strong conviction to nurse at Wyckoff, she would not prevent her from coming. She had been so close to the girl for such a long period that she missed not having her nearby. It was pleasant to think that they might be together again.

By July, Reubena had joined Ellen and became the first woman nurse among too few nurses of any kind at the Detention Hospital. Stricken with anguish when she observed the plight of the sick and wounded men, Reubena was inspired to write a poem about the nation's treatment of its soldiers and it was published in several newspapers nationally. Ellen and her daughter lived in a tent, as did many of the wounded veterans. In the summer heat and the primitive sanitary conditions, as well as the troop transport's landing soldiers ill with tropical diseases and typhoid fever, Camp Wyckoff soon became a pest-hole. The contagious patients were assigned to tents atop a low hill, removed from the general hospital area, and no woman would volunteer to nurse there.

One day while helping Ellen load supply wagons, Reubena abruptly announced she had decided to move her things up to a tent on the hill. Since no one would volunteer to nurse the poor boys in the contagious ward, she felt that she must.

A look of alarm crossed Ellen's face when she heard this announcement and she hastily reminded Reubena of the diphtheria, measles, and yellow fever among the soldiers. The conditions in the tents were abysmal and were certainly no place for a young woman and Ellen could not feel it was Reubena's duty to put herself in such danger.

Reubena, however, told her mother it was just because the need was so great that she was sure it was her place to go there. She warned her mother not to try and stop her for her conscience would not let it be otherwise and her mind was made up. She felt she could never live with herself again if any of the soldiers died because of want of care that she could give. Saying this, Reubena left the wagon to go into the tent and pack a bag. Within a short time, she walked up the hill with a determined step and within the hour she was on duty in the contagious ward.

Chapter Thirty-Four

◈

Reubena's tender age and her loving concern were apparent to all as she busied herself, unstintingly tending to the needs of the ill soldiers. In the weeks that she spent on the hill in isolation from the camp below, she lost not a single patient. Soldiers afterward spoke of her "heroic and patriotic self-sacrifice." Soon the contagious ward was closed, and the last patient departed. Reubena packed her little bag and slowly, very slowly walked down the hill to her mother's tent. When she saw the haggard girl coming through the doorway, a look of concern came upon Ellen's face. She took Reubena by the hand and led her to her own bed, advising her to lie down and rest as she looked so exhausted. She told Reubena that she had heard reports of how hard she was working up there on the hill and it had caused her a lot of concern.

Reubena told her mother that she did work hard and she was very tired. She said she felt hot and cold at the same time, and with that gasping remark, she pitched forward onto the floor of her mother's tent. As she struggled to get Reubena onto the cot, Ellen screamed for help and two orderlies came running up. She asked them to get the doctor quickly, as Reubena had fainted and was burning up with fever. It was only a matter of minutes, but it seemed like hours to Ellen before the doctor came. She had meanwhile hastily sponged Reubena's brow with a damp cloth and was trying to loosen her daughter's tight-necked uniform dress.

As the doctor examined Reubena, he told her mother that he had been afraid that she would break down for she spent too many long hours in looking after her patients with not enough real rest in between.. He praised Reubena for doing her duty and for the fact that she was so dedicated in her resolution to provide the best of care for the sick soldiers. As he probed further, his face became very grave and he told Ellen that he was afraid they had a new case of typhoid fever on their hands. He felt the best thing to do was put her on a stretcher and get her into Columbia-Presbyterian Hospital in New York, where she would get the best of care.

Fear spread its icy cold fingers around Ellen's heart as she heard this opinion. Her beloved daughter was seriously ill. Was this to be another testing time of her own strength and faith? How often Ellen's life had been shattered—it must not happen again; nothing must happen to Reubena! Her first thought was that she would go to the hospital and stay with Reubena until she had seen her through this dreadful illness. Someone else would have to take over her duties at the camp for her first duty was to see that Reubena had the best possible attention and care. Packing up a few belongings, Ellen was ready to leave when the ambulance came clattering up to the tent.

For five weeks, Reubena's life ebbed and flowed in a constant struggle to battle the fever which engulfed her. All was done that could be done to save her. She was often in deep delirium. When she was awake she complained of being so tired; "I only need a rest and then I will be all right again." Ellen never left the side of the beautiful young woman who cried out so piteously when she was in delirium. The other family members were summoned to her bedside, but Reubena often never realized they were present. Nelly told her mother that she would pray for Reubena, that was all she could do. She also said that though she knew it would give Ellen small comfort, the nuns at Sacred Heart were saying Novenas for Reubena and Father Clarence had asked his congregation to keep her in their prayers.

Prayer did not seem to avail in Reubena's case, however, and on October 18, 1898, Reubena Hyde Walworth died at the age of thirty-one. Ellen was completely desolated by the death of her most beloved child, in whom she found such solace after the disappointments she had endured with her other children.

The newspapers quickly took up the story of the girl's passing. The story of the selfless way in which this young woman had demonstrated her patriotism was spread across the country. The papers noted she had surrendered a life of unusual promise in the fulfillment of her chosen task. They called her devotion to duty a proud part of the best in American families and cited her illustrious family heritage. "She illumined the record of her family with a new glory that will never fade away." She was labeled a "saint, martyr, a heroine," and her story captured the romantic imagination of the public.

Returning to Saratoga with a military guard of honor accompanying the flag-draped casket, Ellen announced to the family that Reubena would be laid to rest with a Protestant funeral service. Nelly protested, reminding Ellen that Reubena had been brought up a Catholic, but Ellen told her daughter that Reubena was not at all interested in the Catholic Church and neither she nor Reubena had attended that church in years. She felt that since

Reubena's heritage was Protestant, so she should be buried.

Nelly could not help but ask her mother if she had no consideration for Clara and Uncle Clarence. With that Ellen retorted that Clarence Walworth was a pious sneak who for years had subverted everything she might have influenced in her own household and she reminded Nelly of the grip he had on her and Clara. She even felt he had weaned Tracy away from her by getting close to him through a purported interest in family genealogy and having him assist in his work along those lines. She accused Clarence of stealing every one of her children away from her except Frank and her dearest Reubena. Reubena was the one she would not expose to his wiles.

Nelly felt she could not argue with her mother at the time of death, but she told her the other children would never be reconciled to her course of action and nothing she ever could say or do would take away their own devotion to Uncle Clarence. Nor could Ellen diminish his reputation as a most beloved priest in the parish of Saint Mary's in Albany.

In spite of the argument, Ellen went ahead with her own plans. Company L, Second Regiment, New York Volunteers, acted as the military escort and pallbearers when Reubena was laid to rest in Greenridge Cemetery, Saratoga Springs. She was buried with full military honors. The monument at her gravesite with her name and date of death reads: " She served her country not as man/But better still/As only woman can." Her mother was dressed completely in black mourning and Ellen never again wore anything but black for the remainder of her life in memory of Reubena.

A few days after the funeral, Ellen called Tracy into the library and told him she was not going to stay on in Saratoga but would go back to the apartment in New York and clean it out.

Then she said she would be moving back to an apartment in Washington again, as she felt more at home there and had many friends and acquaintances in that city. She felt perhaps she might do more DAR work again. Her heart was now completely broken and she had so many sad memories crowding around her that she saw no hope for a happy future. She felt she must try to fit herself in some project that would fill her vacant hours.

In a letter written to a friend a few months after Reubena's death, Ellen said: "I have no real thoughts—no real endeavors. I am only trying to forget the 'might have been.' It still seems like a horrible dream; nothing seems real to me. I cannot get back to that other life I left on October 18th. I still see the corpse of my happy, loving family life that I had erected and hoped might have lived long after I was gone. Reubena was my last earthly hope—the one thing for which there was a desire to live on. Now that is gone. Was I negligent? My judgment might have been at fault, but my feeling—never. Love and duty have been unfailing with me. But here is an enemy within my own family. It is a life cloaked in a garb of religion. My own children are polluted—the mockery of saintliness. At least I can take care of my children's property. This is the only thing left I can do for them. I will hand it over to them as soon as possible. It is the only work left to me."

In 1904, Ellen was a featured speaker at the dedication of the Daughters of the American Revolution Continental Hall in Washington. This occasion was to mark the end of her active leadership in the organization she had helped found, although she did attend DAR national conventions in her last years.

When Ellen reread a letter from the president of the Spanish-American War Veterans, she wondered if it could be possible that they wanted her to work on yet another project. It seemed that the organization wanted Ellen, in light of her active part in the recruiting of nurses for that war, and because of the involvement and sacrifice of her daughter, Reubena, to take an active part in founding an auxiliary to aid the widows and orphans of the Spanish-American veterans. Ellen thought for a moment and then decided she could lend her support to that cause for she had always had a soft spot in her heart for women and children and the American family. Even though it had been twelve years since Reubena had died, Ellen was sure she would be the first to encourage her to help found such a group. She could not help but reminisce about what a dear little Puritan Reubena was, but also a thoroughly modern suffragette in many ways, for the rights of women had been one of her main concerns. Ellen knew in her heart that Reubena would want her to help take care of the same women who might be the wives or children of those very men she helped nurse back to health.

On June 23, 1915, Ellen Hardin Walworth was finally set free from her earthly cares and disappointments. In death, as in life, she was remembered and revered for her many accomplishments. One of the early feminists, she belongs to the history of feminism because she helped to push back the barriers that prevented women of an earlier age from attaining their own individualism and personal fulfillment. Certainly she left her mark on her own period of history. She probably would count some of her most notable achievements as those that brought a new sense of national pride to the thousands of citizens who are still visiting memorials, battlefields, and patriotic sites as well as those belonging to the patriotic societies she helped create.

$\mathcal{B}$ibliography

Anderson, Peggy. *The Daughters.* New York: St. Martin's Press, 1974.

Averill Family Papers, Collection of, and Bible records. Plattsburgh: SUNY, Feinberg Library.

Ball, Chandler, *Annals of Hoosick* 1876-77 Annal #20.

Brandow, John Henry. *Story of Old Saratoga.* Albany: Fort Orange Printing Co., 1919.

Britten, Evelyn Barrett. *Chronicles of Saratoga.* Saratoga Springs, N.Y.: 1959.

Carroll, Constance J. *Reuben Hyde Walworth, 1788-1876, New York's Last Chancellor.* Unprinted Bachelor's dissertation, Middlebury College, 1974.

Court Records of Reuben H. Walworth, Plattsburg, NY. Vols. I and II. 1815-17 and 1817-1822.

Davison, G.M. Saratoga - *The Fashionable Tour.* 1825.

Dillon, John J., Rev. *St Mary's Church,* Albany N.Y. 1798-1932 P.J. Kennedy & Sons N.Y. 1933.

Dougal, Mary E. *An American Victorian Family: The Walworths of Saratoga*. SUNY Oneonta, unpublished Master's Thesis. 1979.

Ellis, David M. *A History of New York State*. Ithaca, N.Y.: Cornell University Press, 1957.
Frost, James A.
Syrett, Harold C.
Carmen, Harry J.

Fitzpatrick, Simon E. *Plattsburg - Once Upon a Time*. 1924.

Gibbs, Margaret. *The DAR*. New York: Holt, Reinhart and Winston, 1969.

Hayner, Rutherford. *History of Troy and Rensselaer County, NY*, Vols. I and II. New York and Chicago: Lewis Historical Pub. Co. Inc. 1925.

Hunt, William. *The American Biographical Sketch Book*. Vol. 1 Albany: Published by the author.

Hurd, D.H. *History of Clinton and Franklin Counties, NY*. Philadelphia: J.W. Lewis and Co., 1880.

Johnson, Adelaide. *Ellen Hardin Walworth, Forerunner of the New Time*. "Americana", Oct. 1935, ps. 651-662.

Kirwin, William H. *Saratoga Springs City Directory*, 1885.

Livermore, Mary A. and Willard, Frances E. *A Woman of the Century*. Buffalo: Chas. W. Moulton, 1893.

Livingston, John. *Portraits and Memoirs of Eminent Americans.*
New York: Cornish, Lamport and Co., Vol. 1

McCalpin, Wm, *A map of the State of New York Including Turnpike
Roads* 1801.

New York Genealogical and Biographical Record. Vol. 26 - No. 3.

Palmer, Peter S. *Historical Sketch of Plattsburgh, NY* Plattsburgh:
1893.

Plattsburgh Republican. MF, SUNY Plattsburgh. Aug. 20, 1813.

Porter, Marjorie L. *Old Plattsburgh.* Plattsburgh, NY: Clinton
Press, Inc., 1944.

    Centennial Anniversary of the First Presbyterian Church,
    Plattsburgh, NY, Oct. 1-3, 1987.
    The Past and Present of Plattsburgh. Troy, NY: Troy
    Times Printing House, 1891.

Register of Walworth Mansion 1885-1912.

Slade, John. *Chancellor Walworth.* Paper read before a meeting of
the Saratoga Historical Society, September 22, 1950.

Smith, Page. *Daughters of the Promised Land.* Boston: Little, Brown
and Co., 1970.

Spivey, Mrs. Maude Bramlette and Lewis, Mrs. Emily. Walworth descendents in an interview with Mary Dougall, Director, HSM, September 10, 1975.

Stone, William L. *Reminiscences of Saratoga.* New York: Virtue and Yarston, 1875.

Sylvester, Nathaniel Bartlett. *History of Rensselaer County, NY.* Philadelphia: Everts and Peck, 1880.

Wagman, Ainslie B. and Carrol, Constance J., *The Walworth's : A glimpse Into Saratoga's Past* Unpublished paper, 1975.

Wallace, Evan Davie. *Ellen Hardin Walworth: Notable American Women,* Vol. III. Cambridge, Mass.: Belknap Press, 1971.

Walworth, Clarence A. *The Walworths of America.* Albany: Weed-Parsons Printing Co. 1897.

Walworth, Ellen Hardin. *Saratoga-The Battleground and Visitors Guide.* New York: American News Co., 1878.

Battle of Lake George and Baron Dieskau, 1755. Paper read before literary symposium of NYS Historical Assn., 1901. Kraus Reprint Corp., 1968.
Battles of Saratoga - 1777. Saratoga Monument Assn. Albany: Joel Munsell's Sons, 1891.

Walworth, Ellen H. Nelly *An Old World As Seen Through Young Eyes.* New York: Sadlier and Co., 1877.

The Life and Times of Keteri Tekakwitha. Buffalo, New York: Paul Brothers, 1891.

Life Sketches of Father Walworth. Albany: J.B. Lyon Printing Co., 1907.

Walworth, Hiram. *History of the Plattsburgh Academy, 1811-1871.* Plattsburgh, NY: Telegram Printing House, 1892.
  Four Eras of Traveling Between Montreal and New York, 1793-1892. Plattsburgh, NY: Telegram Printing House, 1892.
  Civil and Criminal History of Plattsburgh Village From 1764 Upward.

Walworth, Mansfield T. *Stormcliffe.* New York: G.W. Dillingham, 1864.
  Warwick. New York: G.W. Carleton, 1869.
  Delaplaine. New York: G.W. Dillingham, 1871.
  Zahara. New York: G.W. Dillingham, 1888.
  Hotspur. New York: G.W. Dillingham, 1888

The Walworth Parricide: A full account of the astounding Murder of Mansfield T. Walworth, by his son, Frank Hardin Walworth.

Walworth, Reginald Wellington *Walworth Genealogy* 1689-1962

Walworth, Reuben H. *Geneology of the Hyde Family, Vols. I and II.* Albany: J. Munsell, 1864.

Weise, A.J. *History of the City of Troy.* Troy, NY: Wm. H. Young, 1876.